£2.95

1380

Aspects of modern sociology

THE SOCIAL STRUCTURE OF MODERN BRITAIN

GENERAL EDITORS

John Barron Mays
Eleanor Rathbone Professor of Sociology,
University of Liverpool

Maurice Craft
Goldsmiths' Professor of Education,
University of London

THE SOCIAL STRUCTURE OF MODERN BRITAIN

General Editors

John Barron Mays   Professor of Sociology, University of Liverpool
Maurice Craft   Professor of Education, University of London

The family
Mary Farmer
University of Liverpool

The political structure
Grace Jones
King Alfred's College,
Winchester

Population
Prof. R. K. Kelsall
University of Sheffield

Education
Ronald King
University of Exeter

The welfare state
Prof. David Marsh
University of Nottingham

Crime and its treatment
Prof. John Barron Mays
University of Liverpool

The economic structure
Prof. Peter Musgrave
Monash University,
Australia

Patterns of urban life
Prof. R. E. Pahl
University of Kent

The working class
Kenneth Roberts
University of Liverpool

The middle class
John Raynor
The Open University

Leisure
Kenneth Roberts
University of Liverpool

Adolescence
Cyril Smith
Social Science Research Council

The mass media
Peter Golding
University of Leicester

The legal structure
Michael Freeman
University of London

Rural life
Gwyn Jones
University of Reading

Religious institutions
Joan Brothers
University of London

Forthcoming titles will include:

Minority groups
Eric Butterworth
University of York

Mental Illness

BERNARD INEICHEN M.A.

Research Worker
Department of Mental Health
University of Bristol

Longman London and New York

Longman Group Limited London

*Associated companies, branches and representatives
throughout the world*

*Published in the United States of America
by Longman Inc., New York*

© Longman Group Limited 1979

First published 1979

Library of Congress Cataloging in Publication Data

Ineichen, Bernard
  Mental illness. – (Aspects of modern sociology:
  the social structure of modern Britain).
  1. Social psychiatry – Great Britain
  2. Mentally ill – Great Britain
  I. Title II. Series
  362.2'0941 RC455   78-41310

ISBN 0-582-48183-X

Printed in Great Britain by
Spottiswoode Ballantyne Ltd. Colchester and London

710 000261-3

CONTENTS

Editors' Preface vi

1 What is mental illness? 1

2 Mental illness and social structure 30

3 Mental illness and the family 54

4 Mental illness: a form of social deviance? 75

References and further reading 96

Index 106

EDITORS' PREFACE

This series has been designed to meet the needs of students following a variety of academic and professional courses in universities, polytechnics, colleges of higher education, colleges of education, and colleges of further education. Although principally of interest to social scientists, the series does not attempt a comprehensive treatment of the whole field of sociology, but concentrates on the social structure of modern Britain which forms a central feature of most such tertiary-level courses in this country. Its purpose is to offer an analysis of our contemporary society through the study of basic demographic, ideological and structural features, and the examination of such major social institutions as the family, education, the economic and political structure, and religion. The aim has been to produce a series of introductory texts which will in combination form the basis for a sustained course of study, but each volume has been designed as a single whole and can be read in its own right.

We hope that the topics covered in the series will prove attractive to a wide reading public and that, in addition to students, others who wish to know more than is readily available about the nature and structure of their own society will find them of interest.

John Barron Mays
Maurice Craft

1

WHAT IS MENTAL ILLNESS?

Almost everyone who reads this book will know someone – perhaps a relative – who has been 'mentally ill'. Despite its widespread occurrence – a recent estimate suggests that one woman in eight and one man in twelve in Britain will be hospitalised for it some time in their lifetime – to understand what causes mental illness, or even to define satisfactorily what constitutes mental illness, is far from easy.

What is clear is that social factors play an important part in its incidence. Why should women be afflicted, at all levels of severity, much more commonly than men? Many studies have revealed that those lower down the social scale are more vulnerable than their social superiors: why should this be so? The search for causes has led to an examination of the relationships of patients within their families, their local communities, and their places of work. Investigations have been conducted since the nineteenth century on the effect on social pathology of different kinds of political climate and different levels of prosperity. Why should some kinds of social situation, and some kinds of society, prove more stressful than others?

These are questions whose answers will take us well beyond the study of the psychopathology of individual cases. We need the breadth and depth of sociology, the study of society, in order to examine them fully. We need to be aware of those factors in society which engender, encourage or inhibit the manifestation of the behaviour we call 'mental illness'; we need to know how the skills of doctors, nurses, social workers and other healers and helpers are deployed to combat mental illness; we must not ignore informal techniques of helping, such as the support of lay groups or individuals; and we must be aware of the grey area of mental illness that remains undetected, undiagnosed, unrecorded.

Before we attempt to investigate these questions, it is necessary to discuss what mental illness is, and what it is not, and to distinguish among those conditions which are clustered under its heading.

Firstly, it is necessary to distinguish mental *illness* from mental *handicap*. Mental illness can be treated and often cured; sometimes the symptoms simply disappear in time. Mental handicap (or its old name, mental deficiency) refers to the inability to develop intellectually beyond certain limits, and is usually characterised by brain defect or injury. In many cases mental handicap is present from birth; it often accompanies certain physical conditions, such as spasticity or hydrocephalus, though those suffering from such conditions are not necessarily mentally handicapped. In severe cases, of course, the child requires constant care and is kept in hospital. Hospitals (or more accurately, homes) for the mentally handicapped are nearly always separate from those for the mentally ill, and their nursing staff receive a separate training, and are awarded a separate professional qualification.

Types of mental illness

Conventionally, mental illnesses are divided into two main groups, the *psychoses* and the *neuroses*. It is not always possible to distinguish between them, but in general terms psychotic states involve a distorted perception of reality, and neurotic ones do not. The psychoses numerically are far fewer, though they are usually the more serious conditions. Chief among them is schizophrenia, 'a severe disturbance of thinking behaviour and feelings, and an increasing withdrawal of interest from the environment; the patient is preoccupied with phantasy rather than reality, and one often finds delusions and hallucinations'.

Schizophrenia is a serious diagnosis, as the schizophrenic is experiencing distortions of reality: in lay terms, he or she is 'going mad'. Within particular cultures, its incidence is surprisingly regular and numerous careful studies in Britain have revealed that in one year about half a dozen persons out of every thousand will suffer from it. Young adults are the most frequent category of sufferer, as its old name, *dementia praecox*, 'precocious madness', indicates. The term was coined by Morel in 1860 to distinguish adolescent cases where intellectual deterioration occurred for no apparent reason, from those in which intellectual development halted or never really started (conditions we would now refer to as mental handicap or subnormality). Morel's patients had developed normally but in late adolescence began to show a progressive loss of intellectual function which at the time appeared to be irreversible. Kraepelin, the great classifier of psychiatric states, broadened it to include other kinds of disturbed behaviour, and in 1911 Bleuler coined the term 'schizophrenia' to describe this and similar conditions: disorders of thought, feeling and perception, which lead to a disruption of will and organised behaviour. Symptoms are confusion, disturbed inner feelings – persecution, for example – isolation, loss of control, and loss of identity.[2]

Schizophrenia has generated an enormous amount of research. One estimate has claimed that by the late 1950s some 5,000 academic papers had been written on the condition, with a further 300 per year in the 1960s.[3] This source of energy shows no sign of drying up in the 1970s: hardly surprisingly, since the aetiology of schizophrenia, and even its definition, are still the subjects of heated debate.

One debate, which goes back to Bleuler, is concerned with whether schizophrenia is one disease or several. Bleuler wrote of 'the schizophrenias' as a group of disorders. In contemporary psychiatry, schizophrenia is often divided into four categories: simple, hebephrenic, catatonic and paranoid. Simple schizophrenia usually starts around adolescence, or a little later, and is marked by shallowness of emotion, indifference and apathy. Hebephrenic schizophrenia includes the additional feature of disorders of thought. The sufferer – again usually a young person – may experience delusions and hallucinations; he may become preoccupied with abstract issues, or become giggly and fatuous. Ophelia has been suggested as a literary example. Catatonic schizophrenia is the name given to a progressive withdrawal from life, which may culminate in the adoption of strange, rigid body postures for hours on end. Paranoid schizophrenia usually has a later onset and is typified by feelings of persecution or, more rarely, of grandeur.

Another debate centres around the issue of whether such a typology is the best way of regarding schizophrenia, or whether such 'symptomatic' approaches should be replaced by a categorisation based on aetiology: for example, the term 'process schizophrenia' has been coined to describe those conditions which are not understandable in psychological terms, and are assumed to have an organic basis.

Even more fundamental is the debate which concerns the very existence of schizophrenia as a valid concept. This attack on schizophrenia has been led by the American psychiatrist, Thomas Szasz. In Szasz's view, the growth of institutional care for the 'mentally ill' led to a situation where hundreds of vulnerable people were put into the care of doctors, who failed to consider the humanitarian issues arising from their loss of liberty. Their actions were justified by the early theories concerning the nature of schizophrenia:

I regard Kraepelin, Bleuler and Freud as the conquistadors and colonisers of the mind of man. Society, their society, wanted them to extend the boundaries of medicine over morals and law – and they did so; it wanted them to extend their boundaries of illness from the body to behaviour – and they did so; and it wanted them to conceal conflict as psychiatric therapy – and they did so.

For Szasz, the building of 'madhouses' was the first stage on this road to psychiatric colonisation. The directors of these establishments failed to ask themselves what should, or should not, be counted as a disease which warranted 'patients' being taken out of society and locked up. From this has followed the hardening of psychiatric diagnosis in order for it to be used to justify such behaviour, and the increasing use of somatic treatment in schizophrenia. There is no such thing as schizophrenia, Szasz concludes; it is not a disease, merely the name of an alleged disease. Schizophrenia's main reality, its principal use, is as the sacred symbol, the totem of the psychiatric profession.[4]

Szasz's theories have received considerable backing, both from influential theorists like R. D. Laing, and from empirical research such as that of Braginsky on people hospitalised with a diagnosis of schizophrenia. Braginsky found that despite the stereotype of a quite irrational 'madman', his patients were capable to some extent of influencing events while in hospital and determining their fates.

They could influence, for example, which staff members they interacted with, and the date of their discharge. In a phrase, they seemed to have all the characteristics of ordinary human beings.[5]

However, not surprisingly, Szasz's views have aroused great controversy, particularly within the psychiatric profession. Roth, for example, writing a reply to Szasz in the same issue of the British Journal of Psychiatry, points out that science advances by isolating and naming entities before they are fully understood: Parkinson's disease existed before Parkinson discovered it.[6]

Whether 'schizophrenia' will ever be accepted universally as a disease entity is probably impossible to answer at present, though the existence of many thousands of psychotic persons in every society is beyond doubt. Research so far has established associations of such behaviour both with abnormal biochemical functions of the brain, and with disordered relationships of the sufferers with their closest kin. The reliability of its diagnosis – which will be dealt with later – is open to question.

An unravelling of the whole matter is still some way away; the question of disordered family relationships will also be discussed in more detail later. As Kendell has pointed out, concepts such as mental illness and schizophrenia may eventually lose their usefulness and become redundant, as earlier concepts have done.[7] For the present, Mitchell's advice is sound: 'Schizophrenia does not exist as such but patients can show schizophrenic behaviour. Thus we should always use it as an adjective rather than in a nominal form.'[8] Instead of arguing over its existence, we should ask ourselves, 'Is it a useful concept?' Even assuming the discovery of a totally organically-determined cause, the social effects of 'schizophrenic' behaviour and the difficulties of management of such people are perfectly obvious. The social environment in which such people live must be considered.

Szasz suggests that the solution to 'being schizophrenic' has a great deal to do with competence, compassion, modesty and patience, and 'the obligation to transform oneself from infant into child, adolescent and adult'. He concludes gloomily that 'all this finds no place in the theories of either psychiatry or anti-psychiatry'.[9] However, at least one psychiatrist has pointed out that late adolescence, or youthful adulthood, are times at which schizophrenic behaviour usually manifests itself, and that these are times of potential difficulty for most individuals.

The young person frees himself – emancipates himself – during the second decade of life from the influences of the family in which he has been brought up. Typically he transfers affection during adolescence from the parent of the opposite sex to a peer of the opposite sex. In patients who become ill with schizophrenia during their teen years or early twenties, the process of emancipation can be shown to have gone awry. These patients have failed to make the adaptations required during crises of emancipation. The causes of their failure may be held to lie at least partly in their circumstances.[10]

The question of disturbed family relationships in mental illness, especially when the diagnosis of schizophrenia is involved, is one which has exercised numerous researchers and writers. Chapter 3 is given entirely to this subject.

Another kind of psychosis is senile dementia, the final stage of mental decline of the elderly, 'second childhood'. Senile dementia can affect anyone past middle age and its effects are irreversible. What it amounts to is that the brain is wearing out before the body. As people live longer and bodies are better preserved, its incidence is likely to increase. One in five hospital admissions for psychiatric reasons involves a patient over 65, and this age group occupies almost half the psychiatric hospital beds.

The problem of the elderly mentally ill is not confined to those occupying psychiatric hospital beds. A recent review of services for the elderly mentally ill makes a number of alarming observations.

A series of studies in Newcastle has indicated that among over-65s, 1 in 10 suffer from either senile dementia or arteriosclerotic dementia. The great majority of these elderly people were living at home. A third of the elderly people had a functional disorder; the majority of these were classified as neurotic and although some of these were rated as severe, few were being treated. Half the residents in the local authority homes for the elderly that were studied were found to be mentally ill; many of them would no doubt be better off in hospital. However, while the numbers suffering from senile dementia and similar conditions rises steadily, there is a growing reluctance on the part of psychiatric and general hospitals to admit them.[1] No doubt, given our ageing population, the demand for institutional care for the elderly is highly elastic.

Other psychotic states include addiction to drugs or alcohol, and psychoses of affect or emotion. This last is among the commonest of the psychoses, and usually takes the form of depression; although a variant is *manic-depressive* psychosis, where sufferers swing rapidly from deep depression to moods of high elation, rushing about in excitement, talking incessantly and incoherently.

It is necessary to distinguish between severe mood swings (psychotic depression can result, for example, in someone being quite unable to talk or even to communicate with others in any way) and mild swings of emotion that are typical of almost everyone. Kendell[12] has argued that depressive illnesses are best regarded as a single continuum extending between the traditional neurotic and psychotic stereotypes.

Neurotic, in contrast to psychotic conditions, are generally milder, but much more common. As well as relatively mild depression, they include feelings of tenseness or anxiety, unreasonable fears (phobias) and reactions (hysteria) and obsessional behaviour. An example of the latter might be returning to the house several times to make sure the gas is turned off. By and large, neurotic behaviour does not involve any distortion of reality: neurotics do not live in a different world, they merely cope rather badly with this one. don't cope as well

A comparatively small group, the so-called disordered personalities, form the residue of the classificatory system of mental illnesses. Among these, the so-called psychopathic personalities are one of the most interesting: psychopaths are people who apparently act without regard for others; they lack a conscience.

Several points arise from this very brief summary of mental illnesses. One is that there is no hard-and-fast line between the 'mentally ill' and the 'mentally healthy'. All of us have at some time or other suffered from the symptoms of mental illness. Although we might never have had the feelings that we were being persecuted by demons, or that we were the reincarnation of some god, we will certainly at times have been very depressed; indeed, it is rare to meet anyone who can truly say they 'do not have a care in the world'. We all have our problems and burdens to bear, and it is seldom easy to translate the kind of disturbance of emotions and behaviour that our problems create into a neat and meaningful diagnosis of one mental illness or another.

The second point is that mental illness diagnosis is seldom precise: this does not mean that diagnosis is a useless exercise. Many diagnoses in medicine are poorly formulated in terms of known causation and treatment. Migraine is one example. Other disease entities remained only poorly formulated until the recent past. One further point is that the boundary between physical and mental illness is very hard to define. Some symptoms – headaches, for example, or stomach pains – might have their origins in the malfunction of our bodies, or in the mental pressures we are subject to. Quite often it is extremely difficult for doctors to tell which kind of problem they are facing. Some physical illnesses – asthma, for example, or skin rashes – often appear at times of stress. The mind is presented with a threat, and the body reveals it. Such illnesses are referred to as 'psychosomatic'. To complicate the question, physical illness is itself a source of stress: any severe illness presents psychological problems, and in some cases the sufferer develops symptoms identical with some forms of neurotic behaviour. In many cases the direction of the causation is not altogether clear. Nervous people often get ulcers. Does the neurosis cause the ulcers? Or is it the other way round? Or are some people prone to display neurotic symptoms because of their personality and *also* prone to get ulcers? We cannot say for sure. But it can make diagnosis risky, and the exact measurement of the mental component of illness very difficult.

Theories of mental illness

The difficulty of separating reactions of mind and body also contributes to the confusion surrounding the definition of mental illness. The association of poor physical and mental health has been frequently shown.[13]

An even more important concern is the nature of mental illness itself. To what extent can persons suffering from depression, delusions, tenseness, or whatever be said to be *ill*? In recent years it has been considered in the interests of the 'mentally ill' for them to be treated just like the physically ill. Powerful feelings of shame and guilt surround any discussion of mental illness, and it has been felt desirable to reduce this by bringing mental illness into public discussion: by treating the mentally ill whenever possible at home, or at least in general hospitals, and by *considering* them as physically ill. Great advances in drugs, and physical treatment such as electroconvulsive therapy, which control some of the symptoms of mental illness, have helped to make this possible. One result, however, has been to broaden the definition of illness, and thus to increase the sphere where doctors are considered competent to act.

This point has already been made in the quotation from Szasz in his discussion of the growth of the concept of schizophrenia. Elsewhere in Szasz's writings – indeed, dominating many of them – is an attack on conventional psychiatric diagnoses. His essential point, hammered home in numerous books and articles, is that there is no such thing as mental illness; it is a myth, and that 'psychiatric patients' do not suffer from 'illnesses' but from 'problems in living'.

Szasz's ally in the attack on the concept of schizophrenia, R. D. Laing, shares this general view; he goes further in raising the status of the 'schizophrenic' into someone who is possessed of peculiar insights denied to others, who must be guided in his 'journey' through madness to an enhanced mental state beyond: breakthrough rather than breakdown.[15]

However, the premises on which their attitudes are based are sharply divergent: Laing's belief comes from a combination of an existential philosophy which seeks to embrace as valid all forms of human behaviour, and a left-wing political stance; Szasz's from a belief in 'contractual' (i.e. fee-paying) psychiatry which would guard against the growth of excessive psychiatric imperialism. Szasz has likened their unlikely alliance against the common enemy of conventional psychiatry with that of Stalin and Churchill against Hitler. He is harshly critical of Laing's anti-scientism:

He has absolutely nothing to say about which madnesses are breakdowns, and why, and how we distinguish one from the other when we see them. . . . Laing has his own categories of approved and disapproved conduct – he even calls them 'sanity' and 'madness' – but he does not tell us, clearly and unequivocally, what they are or how we can identify them.[16]

Clare is critical of both their stances: 'Neither take madness seriously: to Szasz it is a game, to Laing a mystical experience. To those who suffer its torment it is a misery, a terrifying ordeal . . .'[17]

Clare notes with approval Szasz's critique of 'Involuntary Psychiatry' and claims that Szasz has provided a sizeable body of evidence testifying to the disgraceful abuse of the involuntary hospitalisation procedures in the United States. However, this evidence is used to attack the institution itself, instead of, as Clare would prefer, to attack abuses within the systems. There is no doubt that involuntary psychiatric hospitalisation does contain dangers; this matter will be dealt with later. It is also true that the problems of management of the mentally ill remain, whatever the status of psychiatric diagnosis in general and schizophrenia in particular. Recent research has indicated that even in conventional psychiatric settings, psychotherapeutic regimes are undermined by misunderstandings and logical inconsistencies. Baruch and Treacher[18] studied a psychiatric unit in a provincial teaching hospital. They found a lack of agreement about therapeutic goals among staff from different professional backgrounds; a failure to establish the real basis for the hospitalisation of patients; and decision-making in the hands of senior doctors who often knew relatively little about the patients in their charge. Underlying these problems were the contradictions involved when patients assumed the role of sick persons and entered hospital, while at the same time attempts to practise psychotherapy needed the active support of both patients and relatives. The mere act of entering hospital often confirmed the impression of patients' relatives that the patient was 'sick' and thus to be excused responsibility for his or her actions.

No doubt Szasz is overstating his case when he claims that mental illness is a 'myth', yet his ideas contain considerable value when applied to some 'patients'. The questions which must follow are, 'Should the best person to solve these problems necessarily be a doctor?' and 'What are the best ways doctors and others can help such people?'

Other writers on mental illness follow similar paths to that followed by Szasz. An extreme view is put forward by Glasser: 'There is no such thing as mental illness: there are only responsible and irresponsible people.'[19] The American sociologist Erving Goffman claims that mental patients are suffering not from illness but from contingencies. Patients would avoid their 'illness' if they were provided with caring relatives, a loving spouse, a house to live in.[20] Again this is obviously an overstatement when applied to all

the conditions outlined in this chapter, but it contains
grain of truth when the inmates of our psychiatric hosp
examined.

Another American sociologist, Thomas Scheff, sees men
illness as essentially rule-breaking, the violation of social norms.
Stereotyped imagery of mental illness is learned in early childhood,
and reinforced through ordinary social actions and the mass media.
Some rule-breaking behaviour is labelled 'mental illness' and when
treated accordingly by others the behaviour of the mentally ill runs
a predictable course: 'In a crisis, when the deviance of an
individual becomes a public issue, the traditional stereotype of
insanity becomes the guiding imagery for action.'[21] The violators
of social norms are therefore strait-jacketed into their role as 'the
mentally ill' by the response of others. 'Labelling' is the single most
important process in the path to 'mental illness'.

This theory has been the subject of considerable testing and
criticism: for example, that the explanation of *why* people commit
deviant acts still needs to be made.[22] Scheff attempts to answer
some of his critics in a subsequent book, and is modest in his claims
for labelling theory. It is not, he suggests, based on concepts that
are defined denotatively – that is, in a way which allows only a
single meaning for each concept. But neither are psychiatric
theories. Labelling theory is not a rejection of other theories: it is
an attempt to 'clear the air' rather than displace the medical model.
It is a sensitising theory, designed to jostle the imagination and
create a crisis of confidence that will lead to new visions of reality.
A sensitising theory 'may be ambiguous, ideologically biased, and
not literally true, and may still be useful and even necessary for
scientific progress'.[23]

An attempt to deal with some of the confusion that has resulted
from different approaches to what constitutes mental illness is
found in the work of Siegler and Osmond. They present a series of
models of madness – medical, moral, impaired, psychoanalytic,
social, psychedelic, conspiratorial and family interaction – which
imply very different views of the authority of doctors and of the
performance of the sick.[24]

Their discussion centres round the concept of madness, and
does not have equal validity when non-psychotic forms of mental
illness are considered. The dangers and limitations of applying the

to mental illness are obvious: throughout
...ent' will be used as sparingly as possible.
...scription of a hospital inmate or the client
...al and is hard to avoid. In order to further
...ow turn to how much mental illness exists

...ss

How many people fall mentally ill is not an easy question to answer.
All the measures we have depend to some extent on health service
policies or are subject to various techniques of personal
assessment. The methods can be thought of as meshes of increasing
fineness.

Firstly, there are all those people who are in hospital for
psychiatric reasons. In 1975 the average number of occupied
psychiatric beds in Britain was over 108,000 plus another 58,000
for mental handicap.[25] How accurate is this figure as an estimate of
the extent of mental illness?

The difficulties here are firstly, as already indicated, that it is not
always possible to draw a hard-and-fast line between those
suffering from 'mental' and those from other illnesses. Diagnosis
may be made to suit administrative convenience rather than the
facts of the case. Secondly, and even more importantly, the
number of patients in hospital at any one time depends on the
number of beds available. And the number of beds is a product of
policy regarding hospitals: it is no more than a crude index of how
much illness is about, and it is sluggish in responding to trends.
However, certain trends in recent years have made a great
impression on the figures for psychiatric hospital patients. New
advances in chemotherapy have dramatically improved the
situation of large numbers of long-stay patients, who have been
discharged after, in some cases, many years in hospital. Along with
this has come a liberalised policy regarding all types of
hospitalisation for psychiatric reasons, with the proviso that
voluntary readmission can be easily arranged if the patient's
condition deteriorates. This boosts the 'admission' figures.

Indications of the changes come from the fall in the proportion of
the population in psychiatric hospitals from 2.81 per 1,000 in 1964
through 2.31 in 1970 to 1.87 in 1975. At the same time admission

rates rose from 3.28 in 1964 to 3.74 in 1970; they have since remained remarkably steady.[26]

This decrease in hospital population while admission numbers stabilise is statistically quite remarkable. Between 1954 and 1970, total admissions to psychiatric hospitals and units in England and Wales had risen 125 per cent and first admissions 40 per cent. In the next five years the total admission rate rose by only 1 per cent, and the first admission rate actually fell by 10 per cent.[27] This fluctuating pattern of dramatic rise followed by equally dramatic fall and stabilisation suggests that administrative and therapeutic measures are likely to exert far more influence on the numbers hospitalised for mental illness than can be exerted by changes in the number of 'problems in living' that people are facing.

The next technique for measuring mental illness, the next finest mesh of the net, is by defining the mentally ill as the number of patients treated by out-patient psychiatric clinics or by psychiatric specialists. The number of people seeking psychiatric care (involving either hospitalisation or specialist consultation) has been estimated at 600,000 per year.

Again, of course, quite extraneous factors contribute to this figure. If there were more psychiatrists, or if they all worked harder, they would see more patients and thus 'mental illness' would show an increase. Conversely, eliminating psychiatrists would eliminate mental illness. This is clearly absurd. And as Scheff has pointed out, the dangers of diagnosing the well as sick are less than those of diagnosing the sick as well; it is not in the doctor's interest to give patients the benefit of the doubt.

Scheff has tested this assertion in a psychiatric context himself. A series of 196 judicial hearings of psychiatric screening by courts in Wisconsin in 1962 produced a recommendation for treatment in all cases, though Scheff's observers could find nothing wrong with 48 of the people.[28] How likely psychiatrists are to find mentally healthy the people who come to them in a voluntary capacity is open to question.

The third technique is the counting by general practitioners of patients they see in the surgeries whom they consider to be mentally ill. The most recent major survey of general practice consultation[29] suggests that some five million people consult their G.P. each year with some form of mental health problem.

Overall, patients see their doctor on average three times per year. There is wide variation among doctors as to the proportion of sickness they encounter which they define as 'psychiatric'. Various surveys have produced a scatter of from 6.5 per cent to 20 per cent, rising to 70 per cent if 'psychosomatic' conditions are included. However, a number of these studies report figures clustering around 12 to 14 per cent of G.P. consultations assessed as 'psychiatric': in other words, about one consultation in seven that the G.P. performs. These consultations largely concern neurotic conditions; very few are psychotic. The picture of mental illness at G.P. level is very different from that of the hospitals, where the majority of patients who are admitted for psychiatric reasons are diagnosed as psychotic.

There is a very wide variation in the perception of mental illness by G.P.s. The government survey of morbidity in general practice in 1970/71 found a seven-fold variation between practices in the extent of mental illness they reported.[30] An earlier study in London[31] found a nine-fold variation. Variation was particularly marked among the psychiatric conditions that are relatively difficult to define and identify, e.g. neurosis. Variations on such a scale are unlikely to be caused solely by differences in the population of the practice; although such differences are important, as we shall see later. To some extent, doctors who show interest in 'psychiatric' features and symptoms that their patients present encourage this kind of patient on to their books; this process is known as 'selective recruitment'. But it is apparent that it is the doctor himself who decides to a great extent how much 'mental illness' is presented to him. This is particularly true for the non-psychotic, less severe conditions.

Shepherd's study found no significant correlation between psychiatric morbidity and the doctor's age or length of experience though a smaller study some years earlier by Mowbray[32] found a negative correlation between time since medical training and the number of patients diagnosed as psychiatric or psychosomatic.

Other features of psychiatric illness as seen by the general practitioner are that twice as many women as men are likely to earn a 'psychiatric' diagnosis from their general practitioner; and that the middle-aged (those between 45 and 64 years old) are so labelled more frequently than other age groups.

One further finding worthy of note is that mental illness in general practice has apparently doubled between the first National Study of Morbidity in General Practice (conducted in 1955/6) and the second (conducted fifteen years later). In his review of Primary Health Care, Hicks suggests three possible reasons for this:

1. mental illness is increasing;
2. more people are taking their mental illness to the doctor;
3. doctors are now recognising mental illness more readily.

As Hicks says[33] all three reasons may apply; for a precise answer we must await research.

The fourth technique, the finest mesh of all, is to ask people themselves if they are or were mentally ill. Obviously, this too has problems. You clearly cannot ask a deluded person, 'are you having hallucinations or delusions?' and expect a reasonable answer. Similarly, there are difficulties in obtaining objective statements about their situation from people who are depressed or anxious. And there are severe difficulties in relying on personal answers to find out about peoples' symptoms over a period in the past longer than about a month. Many people still feel a sense of shame in discussing their own mental illnesses and may try to disguise such illnesses as more overtly physical. Or they may be confused themselves over whether or not their illnesses are 'mental'. Further, what guarantee of reliability of diagnosis is there if one psychiatrist decides on the basis of one interview that a person is 'mentally ill'?

These difficulties have not prevented large-scale surveys from being mounted to determine how much mental illness exists in given populations. Full-scale psychiatric examinations by qualified psychiatrists are obviously very expensive if given to large populations, so other sampling techniques have often been used. These can include interviewing by non-psychiatrists (perhaps using psychiatrists to evaluate the interviews, or to interview sub-samples themselves) and the administration of question-naires.

The results are sometimes staggering. Measures of psychological impairment suggest that large proportions of populations are disturbed, and the investigation of non-Western cultures reveals the universality of mental illness.

The Dohrenwends[34] have brought together rates of psychological illness from some 35 studies. These display a range from less than 1 per cent to 64 per cent. They quote one study of a thousand rural Canadians, which concluded that at least half the adults sampled were currently suffering from some psychiatric disorder defined in the American Psychiatric Association Diagnostic and Statistical Manual.[35] This study found only 17 per cent of its sample who earned the mental health rating, 'Probably well'. The authors of a study of 1,660 inhabitants of Midtown Manhattan give a figure of 23.4 per cent as 'psychologically impaired' and only 18.5 per cent totally without psychiatric symptoms.[36] A study of over 2,000 in inner London in 1963 reports 85 per cent suffering from headaches, tiredness, nervousness and worry in the previous two weeks. Less than a fifth of these symptoms had been presented to a doctor.[37] Nearly a fifth of a large sample of Americans felt that 'at some time they were going to have a nervous breakdown'.[38]

The universality of some kind of mental illness is another topic which has attracted much research energy. One group who have been the subject of intense study are the Hutterites, an Anabaptist sect living in remote rural areas in North America. It was thought for a time that they were immune to mental illness as a result of their isolation and strong religious belief, but careful investigation by psychiatrists revealed that 128 people, out of a total sample of 8,542, were suffering from or had in the past suffered from psychosis, neurosis or personality disorder. Including mental defectives and epileptics, one Hutterite out of every 43 had suffered from mental disorder at some stage in his or her life.[39] An earlier study of Navaho Indians, renowned for their stolidity and happiness, had shown them also to be suffering from considerable instability and high levels of anxiety.[40]

Investigations in non-Western cultures have similarly shown mental illness to be a virtually universal phenomenon. Careful counting of cases is of course seldom possible. This depends on psychiatric screening of entire populations (usually ruled out on the grounds of cost) or the equal availability to all of formal psychiatric services – along with the equal predisposition of populations to use them. Such services are seldom available in the developing countries. As well as the scarcity of psychiatrists, there is a concentration of their numbers in the bigger towns. The result is that estimates of the incidence of mental illness in rural areas of the Third World are seldom more than guesswork.

One exception was the very large study of Yoruba people in Nigeria conducted by virtually the same team which had carried out the large study of rural Canada already quoted. Despite differences of detail, the authors of the Yoruba study were able to conclude:

By and large the similarity in the two samples is much more impressive than the differences. In view of the contrast between the cultures and life situations, this is truly remarkable. The similarity applies to both pattern quality (anxiety, depression etc.) and to prevalence in most of the categories tabulated.[41]

They point out that such a finding compromises the proposition that different cultures must necessarily produce different patterns of psychiatric disorder; and that estimates of incidence based on hospital statistics only are likely to distort the facts seriously. In support of the latter point it has been noted, for example, that depressed people in Africa may never seek medical help, let alone seek admission to a psychiatric hospital, as depression is considered a quite 'normal' response to certain situations. Psychiatrists may thus be excused having assumed in the past that Africans never get depressed. For a survey of the whole field of mental illness in non-Western settings, the reader is referred to the work of Ari Kiev.[42]

The question remains: how valid and reliable are the exercises in epidemiology which have been discussed briefly here? These surveys have been conducted using a variety of techniques and for a variety of purposes. But answering this question is vital to our knowledge of how widespread is the occurrence of mental illness.

Some of the findings appear erratic on close investigation. The Midtown Manhattan study, for example, used a long structured questionnaire lasting two to four hours; yet it failed to detect 19 of the 40 subjects currently attending psychiatric out-patient clinics, not including them in the 'psychologically impaired' category.[43] And the total reporting of so much mental disorder from the Midtown Manhattan and the Stirling County studies makes one wonder how such societies can function at all.

Psychiatric diagnosis

For the treatment of the mentally ill to be conducted on a genuinely scientific basis, diagnosis has to be both reliable (agreed on by all those competent to judge) and valid (identifying and measuring what is supposed to be identified and measured).

(a) Reliability

It has been argued that the reliability of psychiatric diagnosis is so poor that it is of little value, at least in legal proceedings.[44] Certainly the sight of psychiatrists pleading on both sides in legal or criminal proceedings does little to convince the public of the soundness of psychiatric diagnosis. A series of American research reports provides supporting evidence of the unreliability of diagnostic powers among mental health professionals.

In one study, consultants were less reliable at rating depressed patients than junior doctors, who measured what they saw rather than what their experience taught them they should see.[45] In a second, three groups of people watched a taped televised interview. Among a group of mental health professionals who had been told by a high-prestige person that the subject was psychotic, 60 per cent of psychiatrists, 28 per cent of clinical psychologists, and 11 per cent of postgraduate psychology students diagnosed his psychosis. However, none of a naive professional control group did so; and a naive lay control group all said he was sane. The author concludes that medical training predisposes a judgement of illness if there is doubt; and prestige figures can enhance conformity.[46]

In a third American experiment, eight 'pseudopatients' feigned symptoms of auditory hallucinations and gained entry to a total of 12 different psychiatric hospitals. Once inside, they behaved normally, and although many of their fellow patients were suspicious and often accused them of simulating their 'illness' none of the staff took this stand. All were diagnosed 'schizophrenic (in remission)' except one who was diagnosed manic-depressive. They were administered over 2,000 pills, of which two were taken and the remainder either pocketed or deposited in the toilet. This went unnoticed by the staff. They stayed in hospital between 7 and 52 days, on average 19 days.

Subsequently, one of the hospitals was told pseudopatients would be arriving. Judgements were made on 193 incoming patients. Over a fifth were alleged to be pseudopatients by at least one member of staff. A tenth were considered suspect by a psychiatrist and at least one other staff member. Actually no pseudopatients presented themselves.[47]

Critics of this study, writing in subsequent issues of *Science,* have pointed out that seeking entry to a psychiatric hospital is a sign of illness, and that psychotics are bizarre neither in their every action, nor all the time. But the study does emphasise that clinicians are more likely to risk defining the well as sick than vice versa, and that the criteria for defining mental illness are often vague.[48] A very considerable overlap of symptoms presented by patients who have been variously diagnosed has been reported.[49]

Studies attempting to test the reliability of psychiatric diagnosis have used various methodologies: types of interviews, designs of studies, quantification of agreement have all been highly varied.

Doubts about the adequacy of unstructured interviews have led to a variety of more systematic instruments including self-assessment questionnaires, rating scales, and structured interviews. Each of these has limitations of its own. For instance, in a self-assessment instrument, there is little guarantee that the patient will understand symptoms questions in the same way the investigator intends. Also the patient has to be intact mentally, intelligent and co-operative in order to complete the task without assistance.

The interviewer is himself an additional potential source of error, though this can be eliminated by the use of independent raters working from videotapes or through one-way mirrors.[50]

In the past few years, greater reliability has been achieved in experiments demonstrating greater care with methodology. Helzer's team report in a subsequent paper[51] a high level of inter-rater reliability, using one very experienced and one very inexperienced rater, though it is notable that schizophrenia and depression presented the greatest difficulties. Clinical interviews carefully designed to ensure reliability have also been growing in popularity.[52]

Attempts to use questionnaires, rather than interviews, eliminate one source of bias; but the value of what they can themselves achieve is limited. Are they measuring symptoms (present state) or traits (underlying personality)? They have undoubted value as screening devices: the Cornell Medical Index has been widely used for a number of years as a technique for identifying or confirming clinical diagnoses. The stability of the scores it yields over time suggests that it is more likely to be measuring traits than symptoms. It also suffers from low sensitivity: that is, it tends to miss cases.

Goldberg has constructed a General Health Questionnaire which lists current symptoms and difficulties, and asks subjects whether they have suffered from them recently. It is designed to be used in a general practice setting, to be completed by the patient while waiting to see the doctor. Goldberg reports a sensitivity (true cases correctly identified) of 95 per cent and a specificity ('normals' correctly identified) of nearly 90 per cent in a sample of 200.[53]

There is also the possibility that clinicians in different countries, even if trained in the same tradition of Western medicine, fail to agree on what constitutes a psychiatric case. This has been shown to be true even when only schizophrenia is considered: while agreement is high between British and American psychiatrists on 'core' cases, those 'borderline' cases which American psychiatrists are likely to label as schizophrenic are far less likely to be so labelled by British psychiatrists.[54] This has led to the suggestion that the best treatment for these Americans would be to get on a plane to England.

(b) Validity

The question of validity – what it is that investigators of mental illness are measuring – must also be faced. This remains of importance even if psychiatric rating becomes totally reliable.

Such surveys of whole populations as described earlier for North America and Africa are subject to various sources of error. There is the universal source of under-representation of 'cases' in all such surveys through sampling error or non-response, but in these surveys, designed to discover how many psychiatric 'cases' are present, there is a countervailing source of error, as some cases diagnosed 'psychiatric' may be suffering from underlying physical conditions which the research interview or questionnaire misses.

Further, it could be that what constitutes a 'case' varies by time as well as by place. The Dohrenwends, in the review referred to earlier, note a higher rate of 'cases' in studies conducted since 1950 than in earlier ones. They also subject these studies to detailed criticisms of validity. Under *construct* validity (what is it that is being measured?) they point out that mental illness is defined largely in terms of its symptoms. Symptoms may result from 'transition states' (or personal crises) and these may be opportunities for personal growth, as well as threats to stability.

Some groups, moreover, are put into situations where the symptoms of mental illness are a likely result. The Dohrenwends use the example of American blacks, caught in a system where symptoms of persecution are quite reasonable responses. Many other examples could be used of this process.

The *content* validity is also doubted. Questions asked from which a judgement of 'mental illness' is made must be a representative sample from a universe generally acceptable as defining the variable to be measured. In other words, what is asked about must be a valid measure of what you want to identify, i.e. mental illness. However, 'there appears to be no universe of items that experts agree on as defining the variable'.

Finally, *criterion* validity: what is to be called a 'case' (i.e. the cut-off point adopted) must be a valid measure of mental illness. Here the Dohrenwends make further criticisms of the epidemiological studies, and they quote the author of one that no generally-agreed criteria of psychological health or disorder exist.[55] Indeed, any attempt at measuring the extent of mental illness using the rating of two psychiatrists is a test of reliability, but not necessarily validity.

Perhaps the main conclusion of this discussion should be that 'mental illness' is an extremely elusive concept. Definition, diagnosis and measurement all lack precision. A rigid scientific approach is simply not possible, in contrast to its impressive success in other branches of medicine. Scientific medicine has succeeded in eliminating whole diseases which were common hitherto throughout populations: scurvy, smallpox, diphtheria – the list could become a very long one. Other diseases have been drastically reduced and controlled: rickets, tuberculosis, diabetes. In their place, yet other diseases advance: cancers, sexually transmitted diseases, heart disorders. But the overwhelming feeling is that these too can be conquered, given the right resources: life expectancy has risen steadily.

This success depends upon a disease entity being isolated, a search made for its source, and a remedy worked out. This process relies on the co-operation of the skills of medicine, surgery and the biological sciences. These skills in turn can draw upon centuries of learning, though the addition of the resources of science in medicine on a large scale is a comparatively recent development.

In contrast to other branches of medicine, psychiatry has not had the same success. One of the difficulties has been the hard-to-define nature of many mental illnesses. There is no guarantee that because the aetiological agent of tuberculosis (the tubercle bacillus) can be identified and overcome, the same process will be possible for conditions like depression. There are dangers in lumping together all 'mental illnesses' in the manner of some of the large epidemiological surveys. We have already discussed the unreliability of some psychiatric diagnoses of illness. When we consider the patterning of the different 'illnesses' that make up the whole spectrum, the picture is even less reliable. National differences in the diagnosis of schizophrenia, already quoted, is but one example. The pattern is almost certain to change significantly in the future. Progress, therefore, is unlikely to be made evenly with respect to all conditions: some will be clarified, coded and (perhaps) eliminated, while other new ones may appear. Psychiatric textbooks pass fairly rapidly into obsolescence.

The profession of psychiatry

Another reason for the relatively low status of psychiatry is its comparatively recent recognition as a branch of medicine. The Diploma in Psychological Medicine was not introduced as a post-graduate qualification until 1911. The Royal College of Psychiatrists is a very recent institution.

In the not-too-distant past, the mentally ill were considered as possessed of the devil: their treatment was in the hands of those qualified in interceding with supernatural powers. The insane were generally considered dangerous, and needed to be isolated and forcibly restrained. Only with the unshackling of the inmates of asylums by Pinel at the very end of the eighteenth century, did psychiatry move out of the dark ages.[56]

Much of the historical discussion of mental illness equates it with 'madness'; the identification, analysis and treatment of neurotics is comparatively ignored. There are some fascinating exceptions. Cullen, in 1769, had coined the term 'neurosis' in his attempt to locate the causality of mental illness in some kind of breakdown in the nervous system. Earlier writers had stressed the importance of neurotics in numerical terms among their patients: Cheyne

(1671–1743) had considered a third of his patients were neurotic, and had entitled his treatise on nervous diseases, published in 1733, 'The English Malady'. Thomas Trotter (1761–1832), in his book *View of the Nervous Temperament*, declared that *two-thirds* of his patients were neurotic.

It was with the growth of asylums that the mentally ill became a readier subject for concern. Prior to their appearance in the eighteenth century, most mentally ill people were either kept at home, kept in private madhouses, or confined under the Poor Law, where the emphasis was on cheapness of custodial care.[57] The illness of King George III may have contributed to the growing public consideration of madness.[58]

The nineteenth century has been typified as a time when the prevailing attitude towards the mentally ill of those looking after them has been described as 'moral management'.[59] The idea of *treatment* slowly took hold, as in the York Retreat run by the Tukes. For their patients, the Tukes emphasised the cultivation of self-control: internal control designed to replace the exterior control of physical restraint. But while the thirty patients at the Retreat benefited from a concerned staff and a pleasant environment – Samuel Tuke frequently referred to the community of staff and patients as 'the family' and patients could bring their servants with them –,[60] inmates in less favoured asylums did not always fare so well. As the Commission on Lunacy reported in 1844, the wages for nurses were low, resembling those of domestic servants. And asylum 'doctors' were not always medically qualified: much of their concern was with security, preventing the escape of dangerous inmates. The possible stigma of insanity, and the workings of the Poor Law, continued to deter the mentally ill from seeking early treatment, and voluntary hospitalisation for mental illness was not possible until the passing of the mental health treatment Act in 1930.

Currently there are in post in Britain some 1,400 psychiatric consultants and 1,000 junior doctors. This is less than half the number, as a percentage of the population, of psychiatrists working in America or Scandinavia. Even so, half the doctors working as psychiatrists in Britain are foreign.[61]

In recent years, psychiatry has made great strides in moving out of the setting of psychiatric hospitals and into psychiatric wards in general hospitals. To some extent there has been a further movement into community health clinics. But the great bulk of clinical psychiatry in Britain continues to be done in a hospital setting. In America, in contrast, around half of all psychiatrists are engaged in private practice as their main professional activity. Twelve per cent of the doctors in private practice in New York City are psychiatrists.[62]

Psychiatric careers are likely to involve working in a variety of settings. One account of the ways by which men and women become psychotherapists in America has been given by Henry and his colleagues.[63] A brilliant autobiography of the developing career of a psychiatrist in America is to be found in David Viscott's book.[64] Here he describes not merely the variety of intellectual and practical approaches psychiatrists may bring to their work, but the effect very different therapeutic locations in which he found himself had on his own attitudes and actions.

A tremendous variety of tasks can be found even in routine psychiatric posts. As a leading British psychiatrist has written:

One may be faced in the same day with a brain tumour, a paedophile sex offender, a suicidal melancholic who refuses treatment, and an obsessional don with a work block. The psychiatrist is required to act as a physician on one occasion, an expert witness and possibly gaoler for those whom society deems deviant on another, an authority who will issue orders and take swift action on a third, and a tolerant ever-understanding permissive and non-authoritarian father-figure on a fourth.[65]

Rogow has summarised some of the features of American psychiatrists-to-be that differentiate them from other medical students: they are less interested than other students in the physical aspects of medicine; more likely to have had preliminary training in social sciences and humanities; prefer teaching and research to clinical practice; are more introspective, autonomic and verbally proficient, and less authoritarian, in psychological tests; more likely to have been influenced by teachers, less likely by parents; more likely to come from big cities, and to vote left-wing.[66]

Not surprisingly, in view of its somewhat disreputable history as a medical specialism, and the variety of therapeutic challenges that it faces, the profession of psychiatry contains within its ranks the champions and practitioners of a wide range of ideologies.

Attempts to explore these ideologies and encompass the wide range of knowledge of techniques of helping distressed humanity that psychiatrists possess have in general been timid and disappointing. Most have concentrated on a distinction between physical and psychological approaches to mental illness.

Hollingshead and Redlich, for example, studied the American town of New Haven (population 240,000) in the early 1950s. They recognise two distinctly different therapeutic orientations among its thirty psychiatrists: an analytically and psychologically oriented group, and a directive and organically oriented group. This distinction they base upon training and the principal method of therapy. The directive therapist may 'try to buck up the patient's low esteem, convert him to the therapist's own philosophy of life, give him a stern lecture, offer friendly advice, tell him to go to a resort, to take it easier or work harder, to treat his wife kindly or get a divorce'.[67] Such directive techniques are often combined with organic medical techniques. In contrast, the analytical and psychological group have an almost entirely psychological approach: the emphasis is on the patient gaining and applying insight to his problems.

Kreitman has taken up this division and attempts to measure 'organic' and 'analytical' orientation in a sample of 78 psychiatrists working in two hospitals in London.[68] Unlike Hollingshead and Redlich, Kreitman was not concerned to divide his sample into two labelled groups, but sought to measure 'O' (organic) and 'A' (analytical) tendencies in the attitudes of each psychiatrist. He was successful in finding that the two tendencies did not correlate; they were sufficiently distinctive to be measured separately, yet were not necessarily antithetical. The 'A' attitude was associated with neurotic and introverted aspects of personality.

Other researchers report similar findings. Walton and Drewery, for example, found that psychiatrists interested in psychological process in mental disorder tend to be reflective, self-analytical and interested in abstract ideas; whereas those interested in physical treatments show obverse characteristics.[69] Another more recent study[70] suggests that a conservative political attitude goes with a predilection for physical treatment.

A rather more ambitious attempt has been made by Strauss et al.[71] to delineate three major psychiatric ideologies:

psychotherapeutic, somatotherapeutic and sociotherapeutic. But while psychiatrists who scored high on psychotherapeutic ideology scored low on somatic ideology, and vice versa, the sociotherapeutic dimension did not yield a clear-cut and visible orientation about which strong feelings existed.

One feature of the orientation as psychiatrists revealed by several of these studies is their relationship with work location. Strauss, for example, found that professional staff at the state hospital were consistently more supportive of sociotherapeutic views than professional staff at the private hospital. This difference was most marked among the senior doctors.[72] Hollingshead and Redlich found that in New Haven the University psychiatrists belong largely to the analytical and psychological group, and the public hospital psychiatrists largely to the directive and organic group.[73]

The crude distinction between organically and psychologically dominated ideologies fails to do justice to the range of opinions and orientations each of them embraces. This is particularly true of the psychological varieties, where the influence of Freudian-derived schools of thought has created a great spectrum of psychiatric explanation and therapy; in comparison with American psychiatrists, however, British psychiatrists have been less involved.

Discussions in recent years of the position of mental illness in relation to disturbed family functioning and its whole place in capitalist society have raised the sociotherapeutic dimension: apart from Strauss's rather disappointing enquiry, there has been little in the way of empirical investigation of sociological elements in the values of psychiatrists. In our present state of ignorance, we can only guess at their importance.

Taking its cue from the success of public health measures, psychiatry has become more aggressive in the past two decades, and more willing and able to carry the fight against mental illness out from the consulting rooms and hospitals into the world outside. The idea of 'Preventive Psychiatry' has emerged, particularly in America, and has been carried forward into campaigns for 'Positive Mental Health'. While such forces are to be welcomed as directed towards reducing the burden of human misery, the dangers must not be ignored. Tranquilising drugs reduce overt anxiety in disturbed individuals; they may also act, if administered on a large scale, to reduce the level of creative tension and innovation in a society.

Individuals who challenge the basic assumption in a society are likely to be labelled 'mentally ill', often in the name of humanitarianism. Psychiatrists can all too easily become the humane arm of an all-powerful state, depriving awkward critics of their freedom under the guise of ministering to the sick. This is a situation usually described in totalitarian states, e.g. Soviet Russia; it is a danger anywhere. Szasz, for example, has described the role of the university psychiatrist as police interrogator *and* judge, dealing 'not with the diseases of a sick person, but with the social problems of the college campus'; a double agent serving simultaneously the student-patient and the educational administration.[74] Wherever the psychiatrist serves as an agent of the state, this potentiality remains. The borderline of mental illness is also very difficult to define when the sphere of competence of psychiatrists and other healers and counsellors is considered.

Psychiatry's borders

The difficulty of deciding whether someone is suffering from a mental or a physical illness has already been described. Not long ago many of the problems brought to a psychiatrist would probably have found their way to a clergyman. Exorcism, the 'casting out of devils', was a recognised technique. Probably more people now suffering from the symptoms of schizophrenia throughout the world are treated by quacks, herbalists and witch doctors than reach psychiatrists' waiting rooms.

It is certainly the case that professional groups other than psychiatrists have become increasingly involved in the practice of psychotherapy, and the extent to which they share the ideologies of psychiatrists, or differ from them, has been the subject of considerable investigation.[75]

Three groups of people can be thought of as competing with psychiatrists for treatment of the mentally ill. These are, firstly, others who subscribe to similar secular aims and techniques: other doctors, 'fringe doctors', such as osteopaths or non-medically qualified psychotherapists, plus social workers;[76] secondly, those specialists who invoke a supernatural agency to help: clergymen of every persuasion, faith healers and spiritualists; and thirdly organisations whose specific goals include the investigation, treatment and eradication of mental illness. Obviously, these three are not entirely separate categories: for example, members of the first groups, doctors or paramedics, may invoke supernatural agencies if they feel that such an approach may help the patient with his problems. It is difficult to know which category now best fits the Scientologists, who started as 'A Positive Organisation for Mental Health', but whose adherents may now be placed in the second category.[77]

In recent years, a number of groups have emerged to champion the cause of the mentally ill. Several of these embrace an interest in mental health as part of a wider concern (e.g. the Patients' Association, the National Council for Civil Liberties) while others are specifically directed at solving problems associated with mental illness. The birth and growth of one of these has been described by a founder member.[78]

Mental illness and society

Given that mental illness exists in any society (as has been shown wherever psychiatrists have investigated, for example among the Yoruba of Nigeria, or the Akan people of Ghana) its exact scale will, of course, vary with many factors. In the chapters that follow the main features of the social structure in Britain that affect mental illness will be considered: the built environment, the class structure, the family, work and migration. Some aspects of the social structure will be relatively ignored, not because these are considered unimportant, but because examination of their relationship with mental illness has not so far proved feasible.

The political structure in Britain, for example, has proved remarkably enduring, and in this century, Britain has witnessed little civil strife and no major revolutionary changes on the political scene. This is in marked contrast with most of the rest of the world, which has witnessed the convolutions of two world wars and the crumbling of European Imperialism, with a consequent high degree of political instability.

One exception has been the widespread occurrence of violence in Northern Ireland in recent years. This has taken place without, at least as yet, major social change. The psychiatric consequences of this violence are problematic. Considerable anecdotal evidence has suggested that violence and rioting has led to dramatic increases in mental health problems. Yet one psychiatrist has concluded that no serious increase in mental illness took place during one period of severe rioting; and that existing psychiatric facilities coped adequately with the situation. Tranquillisers prescribed by G.P.s controlled most symptoms of fear and anxiety.[79] A subsequent study confirmed that acute emotional reaction increased among those directly exposed to riot conditions, but that these symptoms were usually speedily resolved. However, an increase in male psychosis and female neurosis occurred in the areas *peripheral* to violence. Anxiety, rather than the actual experience of violence, appears to be the stress.[80]

An even more dramatic set of findings is reported in a second study by Lyons.[81] At the time of the 1969/70 riots in Belfast, there was a significant decrease in depressive illness for both sexes and all age groups. This decrease was more pronounced for males, but confined to semi-skilled and unskilled workers. The decrease was also much more marked in the riot areas than in the quieter suburbs. At the same time, there was an increase in homicide and violent crime, but the suicide rate fell by 50 per cent. While all this was going on, there was a sharp increase in the number of male depressed patients reported from a rural area.

It has been pointed out that admission rates to mental hospitals generally fall in time of war; a similar trend in suicide has also been noted. Every country in the Second World War had a decrease in suicide rate at that time.[82] Fraser points out the short-lived effect of wartime bombing on the mental morale of civilian populations: symptoms were more likely to persist if subjects were *removed* from the areas of greatest danger. Indeed, children evacuated from British cities during bombing blitzes in the Second World War appeared to suffer more from *separation* than from physical fear.

In order to study adequately the effect of war and other social institutions on mental health we need the subtlety of approach and breadth of vision that Durkheim brought to his study of the conflicting pressures of religion, class and nationality on the manifestation of suicide.[83] The chapters which follow will attempt to bring together the information which has been gathered in looking at the sociological aspects of the more complex phenomenon of mental illness.

2

MENTAL ILLNESS
AND SOCIAL STRUCTURE

One of the principal contributions sociology has made to our
understanding of mental illness concerns the relationships
important institutions within society have with mental illness. In
this chapter several of these relationships – those with residential
area, social class, ethnic groups, work, migration, education and
religion – are examined. The relationship of mental illness with
another institution, the family, is so important that it will be
allocated a subsequent chapter to itself.

Mental illness and residential area

It is hardly likely that all kinds of mental disturbance are to be
found distributed equally through the community. The science of
epidemiology (the measuring of the number of cases for a given
disease within a given population) has a long history. It is,
however, seldom totally accurate. Experimental samples of target
populations are always subject to error; until fairly recently, even
census figures could be hit-or-miss; and it still remains difficult,
for reasons stated previously, to guarantee agreement between
clinicians on the presence or absence of at least some psychiatric
conditions. However, enough work has been done to build up a
fairly coherent picture of the pattern of geographical distribution
of mental illness.

Studies of rural/urban differences have seldom been precise
enough to yield a true picture. The difficulties of assessing precise
numbers of mentally ill people (or even the precise population) in
scattered rural communities are obvious, and despite instances of
long familiarity with particular populations and fieldwork on a

heroic scale (Lin interviewing personally 19,913 people in Taiwan), answers to any sort of global questions like 'Are there more mentally ill people in the country than in the town?' must be hesitant. A further difficulty has arisen with the widespread practice of commuting in the richer countries: where do we place someone who lives in a village and works in a metropolis? The distinction between town and country has become blurred.

These difficulties notwithstanding, the Dohrenwends have assembled data on the incidence of some 50 studies, grouped by continent and divided into rural and urban location. Studies of urban and rural communities each yield a huge range of disorder: under 1 per cent to over 50 per cent in rural areas, and 1 per cent to 45 per cent in towns. A most striking finding is the very low reporting of psychological disorder (no more than 3 per cent) from 11 of the 12 studies conducted in Asia.[1]

Perhaps the most influential work on the subject of the geographical distribution of mental illness has been conducted within cities. Pioneering studies were done at the University of Chicago in the 1920s and 1930s. Sociologists studied many aspects of the city in those years, especially its seamier sub-cultures; many social problems were investigated, among them mental illness. The central analytical tool adopted by the 'Chicago School' has been the study of the spatial distribution of phenomena within a city. In particular, the pioneering work of Park and Burgess saw the city as a series of concentric rings, with particular activities concentrated within each. The residential desirability of each ring increased as one moved away from the central business district.

The distribution of mental illness varied too, in fairly regular ways.[2] Psychoses decreased as one moved away from the inner areas, out into the blander suburbs. This was especially true for schizophrenia, but other psychotic conditions showed variations in the pattern. Manic-depressive psychosis, for example, had a much more uniform distribution, with a tendency for the better social areas to produce if anything more cases than the poorer areas. Faris and Dunham conclude that social isolation lies at the root of schizophrenia, and that such isolation is to be found particularly in those parts of the city that produce high rates.

The technique innovated by Faris and Dunham has been applied to numerous cities in America and Britain in the past forty years, with results that generally confirm their original findings. The reports of the Psychiatric Rehabilitation Association, for example, have emphasised the contrast in the extent of mental illness between rich and poor areas, even when these are adjacent areas of the same city.[3] The Psychiatric Rehabilitation Association have concerned themselves chiefly with East London. A typical example of their findings is that mental hospital admission rates for the notoriously badly housed E.1 area of London in 1966 were nearly twice the national average.

Generally speaking, the number of psychiatric patients is far higher in the decaying inner urban areas than in the wealthier suburbs. Moreover, such poor areas are seldom able to afford to provide the level of support that is necessary for such a vulnerable population: indeed, such areas may be marked by a declining population, with the most healthy seeking a home in more attractive surroundings. The population in poorer areas tends to be disadvantaged in a number of ways. The relationship of mental illness and social inequalities is one to which we shall return.

One investigation that is of particular value is the study by the English psychiatrist E. H. Hare of mental hospital admissions in Bristol in the early 1950s.[4] Hare's study covered neuroses as well as psychoses.

The geographical distribution patterns of psychiatric cases in Bristol in the 1950s bore a strong resemblance to the pattern for Chicago twenty years earlier, although there were considerable differences in the relative patterns of wealth in the two cities. Like Chicago, Bristol produced comparatively few cases of mental hospitalisation from its peripheral areas; though many of these areas were relatively low-status local authority housing estates, unlike the more uniformly affluent American suburbs. Further, Hare could distinguish between 'good' (i.e. high rateable value) central areas and poorer ones in Bristol; both produced high levels of mental hospitalisation and both, like the central areas of Chicago, were marked by many one-person households. Hare points out that many of the schizophrenics from the 'good' central area were female and many of those from the 'poor' area were male.

This technique has also been adopted for the study of other kinds of social pathology. The distribution of criminal offences, and of criminals, follows particular kinds of patterns. Again, originating in Chicago with the publication of Clifford Shaw's *Delinquency Areas* in 1929, a tradition of criminological studies using this approach has been built up. One English example is Terence Morris's study of Croydon, *The Criminal Area*.[5]

Another example is suicide. A pioneering English study on these lines was Peter Sainsbury's monograph, *Suicide in London* (1955). A more recent survey has been carried out in Bristol. This study restricted its scope to events of 'non-fatal deliberate self-harm' (in practice 93 per cent were overdoses) and found striking contrasts among the wards of Bristol in the incidence of this event. Its occurrence in some central areas of the city was nearly three times the rate for the city as a whole. The five wards with the highest rates were clustered together in the centre of the city. 'Non-fatal deliberate self-harm' involves young adults, especially women, in many cases. To some extent the distribution of the event reflects this: the central area is where many such people live. Yet even controlling for such a factor, the centripetal distribution remains. Although correlations are found, as they have been elsewhere, with overcrowding and the lack of amenities, one of the most striking features of the high-risk areas is their socio-economic heterogeneity. They include both the areas of high immigrant concentration and those of student bedsitters. A parallel finding appears when the areas of lowest incidence are considered. The two wards showing the least incidence of 'non-fatal deliberate self-harm' are one with the highest proportion of owner-occupiers and professional and managerial workers in the city; and one where although owner-occupation is well above the average for the city, so is the proportion of manual workers.[6]

Studies have been made in Liverpool[7] and Brighton[8] which indicate the clustering of various measures of social pathology in run-down central urban areas. In addition, particular kinds of residential areas have been investigated to ascertain if they produce particular mental illness problems. Three kinds of environments have been extensively studied in Britain: local–authority housing estates, new towns and high-rise flats.

(a) Local–authority housing estates

The interest created by the new housing estates built by local authorities on the edge of British cities in the years following the end of the Second World War was not, of course, limited to their psychiatric problems. It was rapidly realised that the benefits such new environments created for their inhabitants in the form of clean air, low densities and adequate housing had to be set against the social cost of uprooting established communities and the destruction of local friendship and kin networks. A series of community studies that appeared in the 1950s[9] monitored this process.

Clinical workers soon became aware that such areas appeared to be creating as many problems as they solved. A precedent had been set before the Second World War. Council tenants in Stockton-on-Tees rehoused in 1927 in modern dwellings showed a rise in mortality associated with malnutrition arising from the necessity to spend earnings on goods other than food, most specifically the higher rents.[10]

After 1945, influenced by the impression of weakened family life resulting from rehousing given by such studies as Young and Willmott's,[11] two major surveys were mounted.

The first, a study of the recently-built Oxhey estate in Hertfordshire, was carried out in the early 1950s by a team from the London School of Tropical Medicine. Its findings present a picture of poor mental health for the families rehoused on the estate.[12]

There is a higher rate of mental illness by a variety of measures – mental hospital admissions, G.P. consultations for nearly all psychiatric conditions, and the self-reporting of neurotic symptoms – than national figures suggest. The rate for psychiatric out-patient referral was as high as national figures would suggest, yet the researchers were sure that many cases had gone undetected; the true rate would, therefore, have been much higher. Yet the extent to which these figures are directly attributable to the environment is open to question; there is some evidence, for example, that stresses are more severe among the most recent arrivals, and that they are ameliorated over time.

One of the shortcomings of this study is the lack of comparative data. In order, therefore, to test its findings in another location, and to provide comparative data from another kind of environment, two psychiatrists, E. H. Hare and G. K. Shaw, surveyed the mental health of two areas of Croydon, a new local authority estate, and an older decaying central area. Their findings present a picture that is highly equivocal.[13] It would seem from their evidence that living on a suburban housing estate is no more stressful than anywhere else.

Hare and Shaw's study interviewed over 3,000 subjects, plus investigating G.P. and hospital records of 10 per cent of the population of the two areas of Croydon. For most indices of mental ill-health, they found no difference in prevalence between the two areas. Where there were differences, these seemed most readily explicable in terms of non-medical factors such as family size and distance from hospital.

(b) New towns

The creation of 'New Towns', new communities created solely by planning decisions in the years after the Second World War, gave an opportunity for psychiatrists to look at mental health in a situation where experimental control was fully possible.

Two major psychiatric studies of New Towns have been completed. In their study of 'Newtown'[14] not far from London, the authors Taylor and Chave conclude that the kind of planned community they studied has a similar occurrence of mild 'sub-clinical' neurosis as would be found in most urban areas. They find the length of residence in the New Town appears to make no significant difference to this figure, though it is worth pointing out that they treated everyone who had been living there less than two years as recently arrived. A carefully detailed study of the rehousing of working-class families in Oxfordshire from huts into an estate of modern houses in the late 1950s distinguished between the problems they experienced during the various phases of adjustment over the initial two years of residence in their new homes.[15] It may be that if Taylor and Chave had used a more refined category than 'in residence under two years' their analysis would have gained.

When looking at psychosis they concluded that planning did appear to make a difference: the psychoses rate from 'Newtown' was particularly low. However, the association between low rate of psychosis and modern residential area is not a simple one. Few epidemiologists have accepted this finding of Taylor and Chave at its face value: a more popular interpretation of their findings is that psychosis-prone individuals are probably unlikely to move to New Towns. The other study, by S. D. Coleman, concerns the Scottish New Town of East Kilbride.[16] Coleman, who worked as a G.P. in the new town, concluded that the problems of the early days in East Kilbride are unlikely to become permanent: he considered 'transitional neurosis' is a more apt way to describe them than 'New Town Blues'.

Finally on the subject of New Towns a small study by Clout is worth mentioning.[17] Clout found an incidence of neurosis of 43 per cent for women of child-bearing years among those in his practice coming from Crawley New Town. Those eager to damn the New Towns as 'breeders of neurosis' should note, however, that among his women patients in the Old Town the figure was 44 per cent, leaving Clout to conclude that 'neurosis was almost universal for this age group'; a conclusion which should lead us to look towards deeper cultural factors affecting women of child-bearing years than simple housing conditions.

(c) High-rise flats

It is widely recognised that living in high-rise flats produces difficulties, especially for families with young children.[18] Can such a situation be detrimental to mental health?

One researcher came up with a positive answer. An investigation into the health patterns of British Service families in Germany found flat life to be related to higher incidences of respiration illnesses and neuroses. Further, the higher the flat, the higher the incidence.[19] These extraordinary findings have received some more recent support[20] but have been criticised on several grounds: for example, no details of type of access or number of dwellings per floor were provided, yet these are likely to influence the level of neighbouring contact, which is itself a modifying factor on neurosis.[21]

Other comparative studies have produced more equivocal results. Another investigation of servicemen and families in Germany found that psychiatric illness was not more prevalent among flat-dwellers than house-dwellers,[22] and although flat-dwelling did seem a sufficient stress in neurotic personalities to cause an increase in clinical psychiatric illness, the resulting rise in the overall level of psychiatric illness among flat-dwellers was not sufficient to make their rates significantly higher than the rates for house-dwellers.[23] Deterioration in health among rehoused young families in a Tyneside sample was not restricted to those moving into high-rise flats. Almost as many mothers moving into low-rise flats or maisonettes reported more symptoms like 'nerves' and irritability after the move, although mothers in high flats did report more problems with pre-school children than mothers in other types of homes.[24]

A comparison of London families in high-rise flats, low-rise flats and houses, found no significant difference in levels of behaviour problems in children, or psychiatric illness or depression in mothers. More of the families in high-rise flats complained about their housing, especially the lack of play facilities for children. One half of the families in high-rise flats expected to move within six months.[25]

A study in Bristol considered the adjustment of young families moving into variety of new residential developments. Families in high-rise flats showed up rather badly: 43 per cent of the children were reckoned by their mother to be showing behaviour problems, and one in three of the mothers were currently attending their doctor or taking prescribed medicine for neurotic conditions. However, families in terraced housing in the same development showed even higher levels of illness by some measures: among these mothers, the figures for G.P. attendance and the taking of prescribed medicine rose to one in three. Only 20 per cent of the children were reported as showing behaviour problems, yet the numbers of mothers reporting such a child was higher than in the flats. This picture of generally poor levels of mental health in the families in houses was backed by a wide range of other health measures.[26]

It serves as a reminder that however unsuitable high-rise flats may be for the mental health of young working-class families, their problems do not disappear as soon as they move into houses.

All these studies have of course severe limitations. All were based on small samples and all concerned exclusively with the health of young families. We know little about the effect on other kinds of households in moving into high-rise dwellings. And it is often difficult to distinguish between the harmful effects of high-rise *per se,* and effects resulting from defective design in high-rise, due for example to poor sound insulation or frequent lift breakdown.

Finally, such high-rise developments that have been studied have been local authority or service accommodation, with overwhelmingly working-class occupants. The environment of such areas is frequently of poor standard: many of the criticisms made by residents of their homes concern their location. Many of the Bristol families, for example, criticised the semi-derelict state of the area, as well as the 'newcomers' in the population. (This latter remark applied to Bristolians who had moved into the redeveloped central area from outer suburbs almost as much as the coloured immigrants.) They saw their immediate area changing in character, and felt themselves powerless to alter such changes. This lack of power may well be a crucial factor in their dissatisfaction.

In an American experiment, the architect Oscar Newman looked at crime rates in different kinds of public housing developments in New York. Far more crimes were being committed, he found, in anonymous high-rise than in low-rise blocks. This difference, he argues, is not a simple function of height off the ground, but can be related to the fact that in high-rise blocks residents have no power to control or even monitor who enters the areas round their home. Each family retires into its cell-like home: Newman illustrated their frightening degree of withdrawal by playing tape-recordings of arguments and fights in the corridors and public areas of the buildings, and noting that, far from coming out to investigate, inhabitants locked their doors and turned up the TV sound to drown the noise. The concept of 'defensible space' has been coined to describe the inhabitants' need to regulate the entry of strangers, and monitor their behaviour.[27] As Newman has pointed out, middle-class flat developments may have a better-defended entry system, both symbolically as with walls and courtyards, and practically with outer locked doors and even doormen. They are more likely than poorer families in flats to be able to pay for holidays away or to provide transport to parks. The urban poor are trapped in their home environment to a much greater degree.

A final topic to consider under the heading of mental illness and residential area is that of moving house: is such an event stressful?

Many sociological studies in recent years have concerned the break-up of long-established urban working-class areas, and have noted the disruption that this creates among rehoused families. An influential American study has compared the process of rehousing to one of bereavement.[28] However, evidence has been accumulating that a move of house, although obviously a possible cause of stress, is not in itself sufficient to trigger mental illness in previously healthy personalities,[29] and several of the studies already quoted[30] point out the ameliorating effect of time on the mental health of people moving into new residential areas.

One major American study[31] monitored changes in health among a sample of 400 black families in Baltimore who were rehoused into a new public housing project, and contrasted them with a larger sample who were not rehoused. In terms of scale (each family was interviewed eleven times) and cost (half a million dollars) this was a mammoth piece of research, but the differences it revealed between the two groups were surprisingly modest.

For young people (especially children and young women) rehousing (which involved a considerable improvement in material conditions) was associated with lower rates of illness than were found in the control group. These lower rates included those for mental disorders in young adults and, perhaps surprisingly, accidents among children.

However, rehousing failed to produce better health among older adults who were rehoused than among the control sample. In fact, there was an excess of illness among the older test adults in the period immediately after moving in, due to an exacerbation of conditions that were chronic at the start of the experiment. A similar excess of communicable disease was found among the rehoused children in the period immediately after the move: the authors suggest that the children lacked immunity to communicable diseases.

In terms of psychological adjustment, rehoused families also showed modest advantages over controls in terms of satisfaction with their dwellings and the way they got on with neighbours. But few of these advantages reached statistically significant proportions. In short, the overall picture is not one of rehousing producing dramatic positive gains in health and satisfaction.

Mental illness and social class

It is only a very simple-minded architectural determinist who would argue that mental illness rates are determined solely by the kinds of homes people live in, and that beautiful homes will create beautiful lives. Yet it is inescapably true that mental illness rates do differ from one locality to the next, and even from one dwelling type to another in the same development.[32] Differences in residential area are also largely differences in wealth, in income, in security, in prospects and in life-styles – in other words, differences of social class.

The relationship of mental illness and social class has been studied both intensively and extensively. The most intensive study has been mounted in the small American town of New Haven. The mental health of this community of a quarter of a million people has been the subject of three books and countless articles. The original study found significant relationships between social class and the development, prevalence and treatment of diagnosed mental illness.[33] A follow-up study[34] found an association ten years later between social class and treatment status, no matter how the latter was defined.

How typical, one may argue, is the situation in one small American town? How relevant are the findings of the New Haven studies for larger cities in America, and for urban populations in other countries? A careful survey of the literature[35] showed that the lower social classes produced higher rates of illness in most cases. This was true even for Britain, despite provision through the National Health Service of free psychiatric treatment for all.

Details of this association, and speculation as to why such a situation exists, are in short supply. Lower-class life appears to be stressful in ways which produce a whole range of psychiatric problems, yet discussion of these in the British context are surprisingly sparse. Psychiatric disturbance is only one facet of a life-style which embraces certain kinds of crime, marital disorganisation, poverty and homelessness. These multiple social problems are typical only of certain lower-class areas: most especially the disorganised, decaying central urban areas. Broadly speaking, they are not so true of long-established but still viable urban working-class areas, nor are they true of poor rural areas.

Certain exceptions can of course be found: one G.P. who surveyed the mental health of his practice in a community in the north of Scotland found alcoholism so common that it was not looked on as an illness.[36]

One topic that has fascinated researchers in psychiatry has been the association between schizophrenia and low social class. The direction of causality lying behind this association is still far from clear, however, despite numerous enquiries. The question of whether schizophrenics are downwardly mobile socially, or whether lower-class culture is schizophrenogenic, remains an open one.

Much of the work concerning mental health problems of the poor has been conducted in America[37] but the work of the Psychiatric Rehabilitation Association must again be mentioned in drawing attention to these matters in Britain;[38] and a study of depression among urban women, which looks at class differences, has been quoted frequently and achieved the reputation of a minor classic.[39] This work emphasised the greater vulnerability to the stresses of everyday life among working-class than middle-class women, with a greater likelihood of developing psychiatric disturbance as a result.

One writer has suggested that the cumulative deprivations and disruptions experienced in the lives of the poor, and their inability to control their own destinies, are probably factors accounting for the relatively high rates of severe mental illness found among the lowest socioeconomic stratum by many researchers.[40] Certainly the ideas of inability to control one's environment are central to Newman's concept of defensible space mentioned earlier; working-class people are less likely than middle-class people not only to control their physical environment but also to decide where they will be able to live, and endure similar constraints on their work situation. Feelings of impotence and paranoia are hardly surprising in these circumstances.

Mental illness and ethnic group

Cultural factors in mental illness have been demonstrated in a variety of environments. Mental illness in one form or another is probably universally distributed: depression and schizophrenia have been uncovered wherever they have been sought. The use of Western models to account for the conditions, and the search for healing on Western lines, have not however always been present. In some societies mental illness is considered to be of supernatural origin, and priests, rather than healers, are consulted. And in some societies depression is considered so much a part of everyday life that no 'solution' is likely to be sought. The world-wide manifestations of mental illness, and the response of sufferers and healing services to the problem, are too varied and complex to be treated here.[41]

One particular cultural factor, ethnic group membership, is sufficiently discrete to be looked at. This factor has received comparatively little attention in the relatively ethnically homogeneous population of the United Kingdom. In other societies where racial divisions are more marked, such as the United States and South Africa, more attention has been paid to this topic. In South Africa, for example, society's response to the onset of mental illness is determined more by the racial category of the sufferer than any other factor. So 'Europeans' are usually treated by psychiatrists, as private patients; Bantu, on the other hand, are usually treated in the State Mental Hospital or by a traditional healer, a 'medicine man'.[42]

Large-scale immigration into Britain from the West Indies and from Asia in the 1950s and 1960s has raised questions on the capabilities of the psychiatric services of the N.H.S. to cope with the possible new demands upon it. Is the pattern of mental illness presented by these newcomers similar to that of the established population? Do they use the therapeutic services in the same way? What particular strengths do they possess which the services can tap, and what particular vulnerabilities do they exhibit?

A small study of one particular group – West Indians in one area of London – showed a rather higher readiness to consult their G.P.s generally than was found in a group of English patients. Also, rather more of those consulting were diagnosed as mentally ill – one in six against one in eight. This higher rate was particularly marked among West Indian men.[43]

Despite the small scale of this study, it is likely to be reasonably representative, at least of West Indians in Britain. Among the patients in the study, the age group of 26–35 and occupational classes IV (semi-skilled) and V (unskilled) were over-represented. These are typical features of all immigrant groups in Britain. Comparisons made on the basis of ethnic group must always bear in mind the age and class distribution of the population at risk. Enough has been said already to underline their importance. Two small studies carried out more recently confirm the findings that the mental health of West Indians appears poorer than that of native English.[44]

Mental illness and work

The kind of job people do in our society is a crucial element of their identity. When people are asked to say who they are, name is usually given first, followed by occupation. Does the kind of job one has contribute to the risk of falling mentally ill? Are particular jobs a risk to mental health?

Once again, the interest of researchers in this subject has been patchy. Sociologists have, for example, been quick to point out the risk involved in 'spiralist' professions where rapid promotion in the chosen field (e.g. medicine, teaching, some executive positions in industry) involves frequent changes of location.[45] This is especially likely to be the case at the beginning of an occupational career, when the stage of family-building and the development of children's school careers are likely to clash most painfully with the demands of the father's employment. Such families may never be in any one area long enough to 'put down roots', and relationships with extended family and with friends will suffer because of the distances involved. The difficulties are compounded when spiralists originate from working-class backgrounds: acceptance of the new career ethos may mean almost total rejection of that of early upbringing. There may be a further feature of self-selection of the most vulnerable:

All the indications are that modern, urban industrial societies select for mobility through their education arrangements personalities that are extremely open to the stresses they will usually encounter.[46]

Perhaps this pre-occupation with spiralists has been because so many of their dilemmas are the personal dilemmas of practising social scientists.

The process of self-selection is one which has also been noted by other writers when considering the stresses of particularly demanding jobs: deep-sea fishermen[47] and coal-face miners.[48]

Both of these jobs are arduous and dangerous, and mental stress is almost inevitably one of their drawbacks; physical exertion and danger are among the most obvious threats to mental illness for particular occupations, with the combat soldier as perhaps the most extreme case. The sufferer from 'shell-shock' has been a familiar figure since the First World War, although the terminology to describe his condition has altered.

Another threat to mental health, which has received rather more systematic attention from sociologists, is that of boring, repetitive work. Much of the research on the effect of such tasks on mental health has used concepts such as 'alienation' and 'lack of adjustment' which are even more nebulous than 'mental illness'. Yet an association remains: tedious work overflows into other areas of life, to produce widespread minor neurotic symptoms.

One of the leading investigators writes:

The unsatisfactory mental health of working people consists in no small measure of their dwarfed desires and deadened initiative, reduction of their goals, and restriction of their efforts to a point where life is relatively empty and only half meaningful . . . reduction of striving is at one and the same time an aspect of poor mental health and a safeguard against even worse mental health.[49]

The element of self-selection of workers in repetitive, soul-destroying jobs applies too: with the difference that the workers in such jobs can seldom offer relevant skills in the employment market, and may therefore take on such work as the only alternative open to them. And unpleasant and potentially mentally dangerous jobs are often accepted because they pay high wages.

While most of the research on this topic is, like Kornhauser's, concerned with men, the same problems face many women. These problems are particularly acute for girls who go into unskilled manual work direct from school; some of their experiences are well described by Polly Toynbee.[50]

Quite the contrary kind of threat to mental health is posed by those jobs which call for heavy demands on the worker's time and emotional energy. A study of the employees of one American company[51] found that working under pressure was related to job dissatisfaction for both managers and workers and was related to poorer mental health.

Jobs which involve total commitment, long hours, extensive travel, and heavy responsibility must be wearing on emotional resources, although those who volunteer for them must, like the deep-sea fishermen or the coal-face worker, have been selected out by some procedure in the first instance. Not many of us would voluntarily seek out a totally demanding job, and unfortunately for social scientists such people are difficult to pin down to take part in research. Apart from the occasional bizarre psychotic breakdown (well publicised if the subject is well known) there is a much greater liability to nervous exhaustion associated with overwork.

Two qualifications can be made to the psychiatric dangers such workers face. Firstly, the personal contribution such workers make to their job is to some extent under their own control: if they wish to delegate their authorities and spend most afternoons playing golf, this is quite often possible.

Secondly, the voluntary acceptance of an onerous job may be an escape from threat or unhappiness in other directions of life: an unhappy marriage or home life may tempt managing directors to spend even more time in the office.

Another emotionally demanding kind of job is that which involves giving of oneself in emotional as well as in intellectual or physical terms: one which involves interpersonal counselling. All those who share the emotional burdens of others, especially of those in difficulties (people like psychiatrists, social workers or teachers) put themselves at risk. Psychiatrists show this in that they have the highest suicide rate for any profession. American research indicates that one psychiatrist suicide in three is aged under 40.[52] Once again, the cause-and-effect issue – is it the stresses of the job or the selection of vulnerable personalities – remains an open question. Doctors generally have a high suicide rate: it has been estimated that one male doctor in fifty ends his life by killing himself.[53]

Finally, one kind of job which can lead to psychiatric difficulties is that of the person whose occupational ideologies are in conflict with those of the wider society. Crime of all kinds obviously comes under this heading, though a boy growing up in an area where law-breaking is common may find himself at risk if he *refrains* from crime. Other workers that may come into this category are prostitutes, whose occupational skills are berated in public but enjoyed in private; and priests and ministers of religion, attempting to preach and practise their religions in largely agnostic societies like present-day Britain. Other 'legitimate' occupations whose ethos may conflict with the wide society are those of advertising and selling certain kinds of goods not held in universal esteem (cigarettes, for example, or some pharmaceutical products). The life of the salesman may be in fact uniquely stressful, with a constant need to maintain sales; perpetual travel; and a consequently restricted family life. Yet learning to sell also means learning to cope, and occupational skills in this case may be something of a defence at least against neurosis.

Finally, there is the problem of absence from work, which can contribute to mental illness in both men and women.

The problem for men is more serious: they are more likely to have dependents to support, and the workless man is likely to feel stigmatised with the loss of his central occupational role: 'Being thrown out of work seemed to alter a man's social relationships and to make him less accessible'.[54]

There is a related problem for women. The great majority of women marry early in their adult life and are thus released from a cultural expectation to earn a living (though childless wives who remain at home for long periods without attempting to get a job may be looked at askance). Comparatively few women do dangerous or physically demanding jobs or have reached high managerial or administrative positions: those in repetitive, soul-destroying work may escape into early marriage. The chief work problem affecting the mental health of women concerns the decision of whether or not to return to work after they have children.

One problem which has been widely aired is that of the comparatively well-educated woman who, after a period of working in a stimulating and rewarding job, retires to raise a family, and finds this activity is in contrast boring and restricting. Growing pressure to return to work conflicts with pressure to stay at home at least until the children start school. Even if work wins out, it is unlikely that such women will be employed in their full intellectual capacity.

A further problem which is probably far more important in numerical terms, however, is that of the mother who is obliged to seek work as she is left the sole provider for her children; or the mother who is under pressure to earn because of her husband's low earnings. The difficulties of such women are likely to be acute because both needs – money and the care of children – are at the peak simultaneously.

Much of the work on the relationship between occupation and mental health has been conducted in America. Freeman and Simmons have looked at the difficulties of employment of ex-psychiatric patients,[55] and Simmons has produced a series of detailed accounts of the effects of mental illness and hospitalisation on occupational careers.[56] It is well known that even the knowledge of past mental illness can hinder occupational advance: the case of Senator Tom Eagleton, dropped as American vice-presidential candidate in 1972 after a revelation of hospitalisation for psychiatric treatment, is merely one spectacular example.

Mental illness and migration

Some of the investigations concerned with moving house and mental illness, and ethnic group and mental illness, have been discussed in the previous sections. Closely related to both is the influence of migration. Emigration is taken to mean the movement of large populations over considerable distances. In practice, this often results in the creation of a society where the migrant group remain apart from the host community in terms of social behaviour and mores. Often such differences are made more visible by the obvious physical differences between the groups.

A pioneering study of Norwegian migrants in America found high rates of schizophrenia among the men.[57] To some extent this might have been due to self-selection, the more disturbed individuals moving away from their native community. The conditions migrants find are also likely to affect their health. The same study concluded that social factors in the new environment – specifically poor housing conditions – probably contributed to the high rate of senile psychosis among immigrant women.

Contradictory evidence is produced by Clare in a study of schizophrenia among Irish immigrants to England. Their rates were no higher than those for the native English suggesting that the

Irish who emigrated were less prone to develop schizophrenia, while the group remaining behind contained more of the schizophrenia-prone individuals.[58] *age like affluence*

Another factor likely to influence the incidence of mental illness among immigrant populations is their atypical age structure. Migrants are likely to be over-represented among young adult age groups and in the early part at least of migrations, more men than women will probably be involved. It would be surprising, therefore, if the illness patterns they exhibit were not those anticipated from such a skewed population.

Individuals moving very considerable geographical distances are unlikely to do so without some kind of mental cost, added to which problems of cultural differences are likely to be encountered; and further problems may arise if immigrants find themselves, as they often do, on the lowest rung of the social ladder when they arrive in their new country. Thus distance from original communities, cultural differences between English and Caribbean societies, their relatively lowly position in English society, and the effect of the racial prejudice of their hosts, may all have contributed to the rather poor mental health of the London West Indians already described.[59] To what extent these problems are mastered by the second generation of settlers is a question only further research will be able to answer. One American study[60] suggests this adjustment might take three generations to achieve.

Mental illness and education

Little concern has been shown with the effect different kinds of education systems have on the mental health of the children who pass through them (or their teachers). In any case, controlled experimentation would be difficult, given the tendency of schools to reflect the residential area they serve, or the segment of the population they are created to cater for. Thus we know little about the relative merits of single-sex or co-educational, day or boarding, selective or comprehensive schools with respect to the mental health of their inmates. Without such knowledge our discussion must remain speculative.

Educational arguments concerning the best type of system to adopt seldom take cognisance of mental health considerations. Large modern schools are often considered by adults to be impersonal places; it would be interesting to know if the children who spend such a great part of their young lives in them feel the same way. The extent to which the schools children attended figure importantly in their subsequent lives as adults (either as a source of values or more nebulously of identity) is an open question. Such questions are very difficult to answer experimentally.

However, an anecdote may be a pointer. A group of men grew up and went to the same primary school in an established working-class area of inner Bristol around the time of the First World War. This group was still continuing to meet in 1977 – although the school had been demolished many years previously! It would be interesting to speculate on how many groups of ex-pupils of comprehensives in the 1970s will be continuing to meet as 'former pupils' in 2020!

One recent attempt to answer this question has been the study of referrals to Child Guidance Clinics in the London Borough of Croydon. Different schools showed a great variety of referral rates: primary schools varied from 0 to 153 per 10,000 children; selective secondary schools from 6 to 39, and non-selective secondary schools from 0 to 82.

Selective secondary schools had much lower rates generally than non-selective, a finding which could not be explained by their geographical location. However, the non-selective schools also had larger classes, more immigrant pupils, and a higher staff turnover.[61]

The distribution of probation cases showed a similar wide variation in cases between schools, a finding which has been reported from elsewhere.[62] Reasons for this variation between similar schools remain largely intangible: the story of the impact made by a new headmaster on the delinquency rate for one school[63] leads one to suggest that the effect of particular teachers may be considerable.

One research finding that has emerged is that referral to psychiatric services is commonest among children of school age at the time they transfer from primary to secondary school.[64] Perhaps the lack of ritual to mark out such a change in a meaningful way is a contributory factor, as has been suggested at other points of crucial change in the life-cycle, such as leaving school or retiring from work.

The marked transition in status from an adolescent who sees himself primarily as a member of a family, to an adult worker whose identity primarily comes from his occupation, has also been suggested as a particular source of stress for university students. Students have a lower rate of hospitalisation than their non-student peers, though their rate of psychiatric referral is higher. This latter finding might be a function of the better out-patient psychiatric facilities generally provided for students.[65]

Mental illness and religion

The study of the Hutterites, an Anabaptist group in America, has already been mentioned.[66] Although the investigators did find nearly 200 cases, the rates for most types of mental illness were low, and the symptoms of discovered cases were generally mild. There were for example relatively few schizophrenics, and those who were found did not exhibit the excitement and antisocial behaviour that are relatively common among schizophrenics in industrial societies. This relative scarcity of cases, and the mildness of their severity, are attributed by Eaton and Weil to the quality of caring therapeutic relationships available in the Hutterite community.

People who fall ill can be helped by relatives and others in their community (Hutterites live in settlements each of about 16 families) without having to leave home. Indeed, had the investigators satisfied themselves with using standards either of psychiatric hospitalisation or treatment by psychiatrists, as their method of case-finding, the amount of mental illness among Hutterites would have appeared as virtually nil, and the prevailing stereotype of a religious group free of mental illness would have been upheld.

In this case religion appears to have a beneficial effect on mental health: at the time Eaton and Weil studied them (1951), the Hutterites, although living in the advanced societies of Canada and the United States of America, were an extremely stable population, with a simple rural way of life, and a pattern of socialisation which effectively brought up young people to be loyal and continuing members of the faith and their community.

Other relatively exotic religious groups do not always yield similar findings. An investigation of Jehovah's Witnesses in

Australia, for example, finds that among them the incidence of schizophrenia is about three times as high as for the rest of the general population, and the figure for paranoid schizophrenia nearly four times as high.[67] Indeed, it may be that disturbed individuals who are likely to encounter psychiatric services at some stage of their lives and earn the label of mentally ill, are also those people who are attracted to the more unconventional religious beliefs.

It is certainly the case that in a society where rewards are unequally distributed, religions which emphasise justice and a fair distribution of happiness in the next world are likely to appeal especially to those doing without in this. However, religions differ in the extent to which they urge social change: they can be placed on a continuum stretching from those which accept the *status quo* in this world, to those which attempt to foster social change at either an individual or social level.

The therapeutic potential of one group which attempts personal change among its members – the Spiritualists – has been investigated. Spiritualism displays an interesting parallel to psychiatry in that so much of its activity is concerned overtly with therapeutic approaches to the problems its individual members present, and the role of the spiritualist has many similarities to that of the psychiatrist.[68]

A group whose psychotherapeutic ambitions have caused legal and political confusions has already been mentioned. This is the Church of Scientology, whose early development from a central concern with innovative techniques of psychotherapy to one of involvement with social reform measures has been traced by Wallis.[69] Its initial criticisms of psychiatry had brought it into conflict with established medical authority in many countries. However, subsequent indications are that Scientology has curbed these in recent years and is increasingly treated with toleration and indeed respect.

The mental health aspects of the major branches of Christianity in Britain, and indeed in Western society generally, have received little attention, despite the precedent of the use of religion as a major variable by Durkheim in his classic study of suicide. Durkheim showed suicide rates were lower in Catholic countries than in Protestant ones, and lower for Catholics than Protestants in areas of mixed religion. From this he drew the conclusion that Catholicism offered a greater 'society' to its believers than Protestantism:

What constitutes this society is the existence of a certain number of beliefs and practices common to all the faithful, traditional and thus obligatory. The more numerous and strong these collective states of mind are, the stronger the integration of the religious community, and also the greater its preservation value. The details of dogma and rites are secondary. The essential thing is that they be capable of supporting a sufficiently intensive collective life. And because the Protestant church has less consistency than the others it has less moderating effect on suicide.[70]

Investigations mounted on the effect of the values enshrined in the major Western religions have been few in Britain, perhaps because of the difficulty of collecting data, and also perhaps because of the dominating position of the Church of England, and the nebulous attachment of much of its membership. In recent times even the Census has given up asking a question about religion.

Religious affiliation is routinely asked in American social surveys, although it has been argued that the three major religious groups, Protestants, Catholics and Jews, are becoming increasingly indistinguishable in the American setting. A major study of mental health in New York in the 1950s, however, revealed considerable differences between the groups. One-sixth of the Jews interviewed were rated as psychologically impaired, compared to nearly a quarter of Protestants and Catholics. The difference was particularly marked among those rated severely impaired. Yet paradoxically there were also fewer Jews among the groups rated as psychologically well. Jews had higher rates among those who had received psychiatric treatment. It seems, then, that Jews, while perhaps suffering less from mental illness, made greater use of psychiatric services. This thesis received confirmation from a question asked about how informants would respond to a hypothetical problem in the family. Just under half the Jews said they would involve a psychotherapist, against just under a third of the Protestants and a quarter of the Catholics.[71]

Reasons for the overall superiority of the Jews in this study in avoiding serious mental health problems must be speculative. Perhaps Jewish culture provides a stronger defence against the stresses of childhood, or simply a greater 'society' in the Durkheimian sense. Perhaps the condition of almost permanent 'exile' has forged a high level of psychological toughness. Perhaps Jewish values simply blend better with the overall ethos of New York. Until more comparative data is available these thoughts must remain speculations.

If church membership and attendance continue to fall, the question that should be asked is not 'How do the different religions contribute to or defend themselves against mental illness?' but 'Can societies operate with a satisfactory level of mental health, but without any widespread religious practices or even belief in God?' The mental health of agnostic or atheistic societies is an even more open question than those we have been attempting to answer. The world has never seen one before, and as yet history provides no guidelines.

3

MENTAL ILLNESS
AND THE FAMILY

In many cases of mental illness, family relationships are distorted, and marked by conflict and aggression. Some kinds of mental illness and some kinds of disturbed family relationships have been the subject of considerable speculation and research in recent years, leading to the claims of some schools of psychiatry that the basis of all mental illness is to be found in the family. In contrast, other psychiatrists remain unimpressed by such assertions; and other aspects of mental illness involving a disturbance of family relationships have received comparatively little investigation.

Two of the most influential ideas in this field have been those of maternal deprivation, and the double-bind.

Maternal deprivation

The first user of the term 'maternal deprivation' was John Bowlby. Bowlby's earliest major work concerned the social and emotional background of juvenile thieves. It demonstrated an association between the 'affectionless character' shown by some of the most persistent of them and early severely depriving separation experiences. Bowlby suggested that experiences of this nature may be foremost among the causes of 'delinquency character formation'.

His later book, *Maternal Care and Mental Health*,[1] elaborated on this work, developing the central idea of 'maternal deprivation'.

What is believed to be essential for mental health is that an infant and young child should experience a warm, intimate and continuous relationship with his mother, or permanent mother substitute, in which both find satisfaction and enjoyment.

Maternal deprivation results from failure to develop such a relationship and is a serious threat to emotional well-being and mental health. Bowlby's ideas reached a wide and responsive audience, and *Maternal Care and Mental Health* has become, in its edited form and under the title *Child Care and the Growth of Love*, a constantly reprinted paperback. Bowlby has elaborated his ideas on attachment and loss into subsequent books.

Bowlby claimed that his work demonstrated that maternal care in infancy and early childhood was essential for mental health. It was a discovery the importance of which he claimed 'may be compared to that of the role of vitamins in physical health', and Barbara Wootton has likened its importance to Elizabeth Fry's exposure of the insanitary conditions in prisons in the nineteenth century.[2]

Bowlby's work has also stimulated a huge amount of research, which Rutter has drawn together.[3] Rutter notes the now well documented association that harmful early life experiences are likely to have serious adverse effects on later life experience. Included in this finding can be counted the distress of children entering hospital or residential nursery; developmental retardation following admission to a residential institution where care provided is of low emotional quality; the association of delinquency and broken homes; affectionless psychopathy following multiple separation in early childhood; and even dwarfism (extremely short stature and delayed skeletal and sexual maturation) in children who have experienced extreme deprivation.

Rutter is careful to point out that 'maternal deprivation' covers a wide range of different experiences, and that while associations with various forms of pathology have been established, the psychological mechanisms which are brought into play can only be suggested.

It has been hypothesised that the syndrome of acute distress is probably due in part to a disruption of the bonding process (not necessarily with the mother): developmental retardation and intellectual impairment are both a consequence of privation of perceptual and linguistic experience; dwarfism is usually due to nutritional privation; enuresis is sometimes a result of stressful experiences in the first five years; delinquency follows family discord; and psychopathy may be the end product of a failure to develop bonds or attachments in the first three years of life. None of these suggestions has as yet got firm and unequivocal empirical support and it is important to remember that they remain hypotheses which require rigorous testing. What is important is that it is now clear that the different elements in a child's early life experiences play quite different parts in the development process . . .[4]

Bowlby's orientation is psycho-analytical, and his original insight has tended to focus attention on one level of loss: that of the mother, the 'feminine' or 'expressive' aspect of parenthood. Despite criticisms and misunderstandings, his influence has been immense. However, other potentially harmful disruptions in childhood have been relatively ignored.

For example, the loss of a father may have severe and adverse effects on the growing child. Paternal deprivation is likely to be serious if it occurs at a rather later stage of development than Bowlby studied: for example, in the years between 3 and 7, when the child is being gradually socialised into the adult world of rules and logic, and the peer world of the school. Loss of a father at this stage may not only inhibit the moral development of the child, but may produce anxieties and tensions in the mother leading to a doubly disadvantaged childhood.

Research has established a link between broken homes, deviant or absent fathers, and maternal deprivation, with the delinquent behaviour of sons.[5] The link between an absent father and mental illness or severe deprivation in children has not been securely established. Very little work has been done on the subject, and most of it has been on a small scale. There remains the related question of the effect on children of having a father at home who is less than effective in his role. One study of family ill-health found disturbed behaviour in children to be significantly commoner if the father was neurotic, but found no association between behaviour disorder in the child and neurosis in the mother,[6] although other research has found no association between children's behaviour problems and father's mental health.[7] The paucity of investigation is surprising considering the numbers of young children growing up in contemporary western society in one-parent (usually fatherless) households.

Adolescence and the double-bind

Another relationship which has excited interest within psychiatry, and to an even greater extent among social scientists working around the fringe of psychiatry, has been that between emotionally disturbed teenagers and their parents. This has been described most pointedly in the writings of the existentialist psychiatrist, R. D. Laing, and, in the field of clinical psychiatry, is most relevant to the situation of teenage schizophrenics. The whole field of family relationships and schizophrenia has been a most active one in terms of the research output of psychiatrists and social scientists. Several hundred empirical studies have been carried out. They are brought together and assessed in a thorough fashion by Hirsch and Leff, two psychiatrists, in their book, *Abnormalities in Parents of Schizophrenics*.[8]

The main purpose of Hirsch and Leff's book is to assess the importance of the parents' contribution to the aetiology of schizophrenia. They traced the association noted by research in the 1930s between 'over-protection' practised by the parents and the diagnosis of weakness or anomaly in the children. In 1948 Frieda Fromm-Reichmann coined the phrase 'schizophrenogenic mother' which dominated thinking about familial process in schizophrenia for many years. Much of the subsequent work portraying the mothers of schizophrenics as overprotecting and domineering, Hirsch and Leff claim, is methodologically dubious; and they point out that excessive protectiveness in the mother may develop as a response to an abnormal child, rather than the reverse. They conclude from other studies that the parents of schizophrenics show more marital disharmony than other parents.

One discussion of the relationship of the parents of schizophrenics that has received particular attention is their relative dominance. Hirsch and Leff note an association revealed by several researchers between poor premorbid personality in the patient and dominance by the parent of opposite sex to the patient. Generally, however, the dominance patterns of the parents of schizophrenics do not differ from normal families.

One of the concepts applied to the family functioning of schizophrenics in recent years has been the 'double-bind'. This term was coined by Bateson and his co-workers in 1956 to describe the impossible emotional position which many schizophrenics were driven into by the conflicting content of messages given to them by those emotionally close to them. Schizophrenia results from the inability of the recipient to handle these messages in such a way that the conflict is resolved.[9]

Essentially the double-bind is a situation where the victim is punished if he indicates love and affection and punished if he does not, in the relationship that is most important of all to him and the model for all other relationships. Usually the relationship described is that of the patient and his or her mother. An essential part of the double-bind situation is that the victim's escape routes, such as gaining the support of other members of the family, are cut off. Fathers, brothers and sisters typically offer no support to the patient and may collude with the mother against him. As Bateson points out earlier in the same article 'It is likely that the fathers of schizophrenics are not substantial enough to lean on'.

Bateson quotes the case of a young man fairly well recovered from a schizophrenic episode who was visited in hospital by his mother. He was glad to see her and impulsively put his arm round her shoulders, whereupon she stiffened. He withdrew his arm and she asked 'Don't you love me any more?' He then blushed and she said 'Dear, you must not be so easily embarrassed and afraid of your feelings'.

The patient is criticised by his mother for showing affection, for what in fact amounts to his mother's own faults. If he had not shown affection, he would have been criticised for that instead. He is unable to withdraw from this situation and comment upon it objectively; he is unlikely to get support from other members of the family.

Conflict within families is virtually a universal phenomenon: the question of how often, how severe and how typical is conflict in families which do not produce a schizophrenic member, has never systematically been asked. Most research has been conducted with families already caught in the clinical net. Sedgwick has described what has been going on.

The pathology of family communication has become one of the great research enterprises of American science. Hundreds of families have trooped into the laboratories of academic institutions and hospitals, there to have their entire verbal output tape-recorded over many sessions, their gestures and eye movements filmed and their biographies unearthed in depth by interdisciplinary panels of doctors, psychologists, sociologists and technicians.

The families inhabit the select theatre for a period of hours or days, enacting a kind of real life TV serial, based on the usual domestic interchange, and then depart. They leave behind them a mass of sound-tracks, video tapes, behaviour checklists, completed test sheets and other revelatory material, a huge deposit of past praxis, which is then worked over for months by a bureau of investigators, and in due course, delivered to the interested public as a journal article.

The cumulative bibliography of the Schizophrenic Family forms a veritable saga of modern home life running in repeated instalments through some half dozen scholarly channels over about fifteen past years, with no end point yet in sight.[10]

Later in the same article Sedgwick gives a description of a typical double-bind family which verges on parody. Instances of deception, collusion, and scape-goating, all essential elements of the double-bind, occur in almost all families. Existing research says little, therefore, to clarify why some families and not others produce a member who is ultimately diagnosed as schizophrenic. Some families are, as Lomas[11] has pointed out, simply more interested in themselves than others. Hirsch and Leff conclude, 'There is no evidence that double-bind interactions are more common in the families of schizophrenics than other families',[12] though they quote evidence from an American study which suggests that the fathers of upper-class schizophrenics may be unduly submissive.[13]

In the last decade the idea of double-bind and schizophrenogenic family situations has reached a wide audience, in particular through the writings of R. D. Laing.

Much of Laing's writing falls more into the field of existentialist philosophy than mental illness, and as such is of only marginal interest here. But his work on families of schizophrenics conducted with Esterson[14] is of great relevance.

Laing and Esterson are among those who contend that there is no such illness as schizophrenia. They present 11 case studies of patients diagnosed as such, arguing that an understanding of the family dynamics in each case shows the behaviour of the 'patient' to be a rational – perhaps the only available – path of response to the stressful and conflicting pressures to which she was subjected. (All the patients were young women between the age of 15 and 40.)

As an unravelling of erroneous interpersonal human communication, making psychotic behaviour intelligible, the book is a masterly account; as a contribution towards an understanding of what constitutes schizophrenia, it has many shortcomings. Why are the subjects 'chosen' for schizophrenia, and not other family members? Is their behaviour not simply an exaggeration of the more 'expressive' emotion-bearing role of women common in our society? Or an exaggeration of the rebellion against parental authority, that characterises so many families when children reach adolescence? Crucially, what is the difference between the dynamics of the families described by Laing and Esterson and others at a similar stage of the life-cycle? The original edition of *Sanity, Madness and the Family* was sub-titled, 'Volume I: Families of Schizophrenics'. Sadly, Volume II has never appeared. Laing has been accused of romanticising schizophrenia by confusing it with the natural rebelliousness of the young. Schizophrenia has been romanticised in the twentieth century as tuberculosis was in the nineteenth.[15] In fairness to Laing and Esterson, they do not claim to have set out to 'solve' schizophrenia, as they make clear in the preface to the second edition of their book.

What in fact is precisely the *trouble* faced by these 11 young women? According to Collier,[16] the typical victim is a young person who has not escaped from her family of origin. Insofar as the child conforms to the pattern laid down for it by the unconscious fantasies of its parents, it is rewarded by the confirmation of its experience. Most of the subjects in Laing's book had been trained never to trust people outside the family. The privatisation of family life has been with them too successfully achieved.

The questions Laing's work leads us to, argues Collier, are formed by asking why some families produce madness and others do not. But rather than looking at the processes whereby some individuals are disturbed, we should consider the social causes of disturbed families. However, it seems quite unreasonable, as Collier hints, to 'blame' capitalism for this disturbance: there would appear to be no reason why family constellations such as Laing describes should not be found in, say, the socialist countries of Eastern Europe – though investigating them and publishing books about them might be much more difficult in such political climates.

Laing's influence has spread beyond the study of mental illness; much of what he has to say elsewhere is of interest in other fields. Perhaps more surprisingly, his books have reached a wide lay readership, bringing together an unlikely alliance of unorthodox psychiatrists wishing to bash their more conventional colleagues, social scientists wishing to do the same to the medical model of mental illness, articulate patients wanting ammunition against their therapists, teenagers and young adults unhappy in their families and with authority figures generally, and radical politicians wishing to attack the established political system. He has undoubtedly influenced the thought of all these groups and has certainly made therapists more careful in their assessment of the family background and communication patterns of many of their patients.

By concentrating on one particular kind of problem and basing their thoughts upon such a small group, Laing and Esterson behave in a highly 'unscientific' way, but they are following a long tradition, going back at least to Freud.[17] Perhaps they underestimate the influence that children can have upon their parents: even a crying baby soon learns how it can influence its mother's actions. But if Laing's work has one major shortcoming, it is that picked out by one of his most perceptive critics, 'What is finally lacking in Laing's view . . . is . . . an essential respect for evil and cruelty as just as real and human as love and growth'.[18]

The work of Wynne and Singer has demonstrated that defects in communication are present in parents of schizophrenics, and absent in control parents.[19] But their study is exploratory; Hirsch and Leff point out shortcomings in aspects of its methodology. They themselves have attempted to replicate Wynne and Singer's findings. In order to introduce greater methodological rigour, they used as controls neurotic psychiatric patients, whom Wynne and Singer had found occupied an intermediate position between schizophrenics and normals on their scales of communication.

Their results indicate similar distributions in the patterning of communication defects, but only if Hirsch and Leff had included a category of patients as 'borderline' between schizophrenia and neurosis. They themselves argue that the fathers of schizophrenics in their English study showed markedly different responses from Wynne and Singer's, and thus Wynne and Singer's findings are not replicated.

Hirsch and Leff's aim in their own study was the modest one of contrasting communication defects among the parents of schizophrenics and neurotics. The meaning of schizophrenia as a diagnosis, and its ultimate cause (if such a thing exists) are still open to question. Alternative approaches, via the pathology of biochemical mechanisms, have achieved considerable success.

Hirsch and Leff do not discuss this alternative approach, but state, almost casually, after an extended discussion of family studies, that 'a genetic factor in the transmission of schizophrenia has been satisfactorily established'. Yet the very diagnosis of schizophrenia is itself far from universally agreed as Hirsch and Leff themselves mention.[20] While the family relationships of patients described as schizophrenic are undoubtedly more disturbed than the norm, the question of causes of schizophrenia, and even to some extent its isolation as a disease entity, is still open.

Autism

One group of patients have created a great deal of interest in recent years. Their condition has certain similarities with that of schizophrenics. These are children who withdraw from most types of communication into their own private world: whose diagnosis is autism.

The condition of autism has a history going back to the case of a boy aged about 12 living in woods in Aveyron, France, in 1799. The boy could not speak and had apparently been living without any form of human contact for as long as anyone knew. Caught and put into the care of understanding and skilful people, he never learned to speak; but he did learn to behave in socially acceptable ways, to read, and to communicate with others in non-verbal ways.

The condition was first recognised in modern times by Kanner, who described in a sample of 11 children the extraordinary range of sensory and cognitive malfunctioning that accompanied what appeared to be normal intelligence and physical development.

The condition is difficult to define precisely, but surveys have indicated it afflicts one child in about 5,000. Boys suffer more often than girls, and the children of higher social classes may be over-represented. Identifiable neurological abnormalities have been found in a substantial minority of afflicted children, but a great deal about all aspects of the condition remains unknown.[21]

The relatively high appeal as research topics of maternal deprivation (Rutter lists over 400 references), family communication in schizophrenia (Hirsch and Leff list over 200), and autism

(Wing lists nearly 300) has not been matched in other areas of disturbed family functioning. The vulnerability of family life is demonstrated in many ways, some directly leading to mental illness, some more tangentially relevant.

Children of mentally ill parents

One American study[22] has reported in depth on the psychiatric problems that childbirth itself creates, which has led to hospital practices of joint admissions of mothers and babies. Motherhood is an event for which full experiential preparation is quite impossible. For the first time in her life, a mother is totally subservient to the needs of another person – her baby. As well as stressing the problems, both practical and psychological, that stem from the isolation of the nuclear family, Grunebaum and his colleagues found that birth complications were a significant source of stress, and that boy babies were more likely to create difficulties than girl babies.

Mental health problems of some children, therefore, start as soon as they are born. A research study of the children of sick parents has been made by Rutter.[23] Difficulties arose from both physical and mental parental ill-health. The involvement of the child in the symptoms of the parent's mental illness is particularly dangerous. An American study of depressed women has noted that they experience considerable friction with their children when contrasted with a control group.[24] As Rutter points out, keeping mentally ill people out of hospital whenever possible is praiseworthy, but the risk to other family members should not be overlooked. Wolff[25] provides an excellent survey of the stressful situations of childhood.

Family violence

Violence within the family has become a commonplace event. As an example, the murder by a man of his wife and children, or by a woman of her children, have formed a high proportion of all murders in recent years. Frequently such crimes are followed by suicide of the murderer. One review of 131 cases of parental murder found that 60 per cent of the murderers were psychotic and over half suffering from depression.[26]

A related phenomenon concerns violence, short of murder, committed by parents on their children, in many cases occurring when the child is very young. Here there are obvious difficulties in establishing the facts of the case. The child may be too young to give evidence or too frightened; parents may collude in stories of accidental injuries. Indeed, the whole phenomenon was dismissed for many years, with explanations that some children had brittle bones, or were accident-prone.

A number of investigations have been mounted in recent years on the subject of child abuse, following several cases which revealed breakdowns in communication among the various agencies which were attempting to help the families in question. These investigations[27] have revealed that in many cases such attacks on children occur where parents are in poor material circumstances, young, and of low intelligence. To what extent is mental illness a factor in these assaults? The answer to this question depends on how low a threshold to stress is equated with mental illness. Low thresholds to stress are themselves a result of low personal strengths, or high environmental pressures, or both. This is a subject to be returned to later, in a discussion on neurosis and family relationships. But undoubtedly a minority of parents who assault their children have bizarre and/or aggressive personalities and can be considered as mentally ill. Such parents are those who inflict injuries of a sadistic nature on their children: for example, burning them with cigarettes. In most cases, aggression against children results from an inability to cope, rather than sadism.

Violence by husbands against wives is another phenomenon which has burst into public consciousness only recently. Again the equation of such violence with mental illness must not be made too glibly. In some social environments, even until very recently, wives were treated as persons of strictly limited rights. The acceptance of physical aggression from drunken husbands was part of their lot. The newly-found confidence of women has not suddenly changed the behaviour of their husbands, but it has lowered the threshold of violence which the wives will tolerate: and the creation of refuges for battered wives by Erin Pizzey and her followers have given them a place to go.

Family isolation

The isolation of the nuclear family and the fragility of the marriage relationship are now sociological clichés which express some of the vulnerabilities which threaten cohesive family life. What is surprising is that the links between these social changes, and changes in the epidemiology of mental illness, have remained largely unexplored. The psychic cost of nuclear family isolation is likely to fall principally on the wife/mother and indirectly on the children. Attention was drawn to this first by Young and Willmott, in their study of rehousing families in East London already referred to (see Chapter 2). Difficulties of young families (especially of the mothers) are not, however, restricted to areas where a great deal of rehousing has taken place. Already established large housing estates (such as Dagenham, described by Willmott in a later book) force mobility upon growing families, as no small dwellings are available for small households in the early years of marriage. Some types of small dwellings (e.g. high-rise flats) are clearly unsuitable for households including pre-school children. At the same time, the 'doubling-up' of households with children continuing to live with their parents after marriage is considered universally to be unsatisfactory.

The reasons for this are not immediately apparent. In some cultures, households consisting of extended families live together harmoniously. Not only may women of more than one generation share domestic duties, but more than one woman may share the same husband. Expectations in urban industrial society are, however, that each adult may have a whole married partner to themselves, and that each nuclear family unit may have its own separate household: alternative arrangements are seldom satisfactory.

The burden that is created, especially for the wife/mother, is tremendous. Very high rates of neurosis for women with young children have been reported in the studies by Clout, and Brown et al., mentioned earlier. Such mothers are deprived of the company of their traditionally greatest support, their own mother. In some cases, their husband's career may involve extensive geographical mobility, and the couple may move several hundred miles away from the wife's parental home, even to another continent. Much more commonly, however, young working-class couples will move to another district in the same city, in order to obtain adequate housing: the subjective experience of such a separation (in terms of coping with toddlers, buses and prams) may make it more total separation than the car-owning, telephone-using, middle-class wife who moves from one city to another.

At the same time, little may have been done to compensate for such a loss. Motherhood is likely to impose a heavy burden. Contemporary families are small, and young women may have had little experience of living with babies or small children. Young wives may have no relatives within walking distance and may lack the social skills to achieve a satisfactory blend of intimacy and social distance with neighbours. They may be unlikely to have experienced (or even to have witnessed others experiencing) the kind of heavy demands made by tiny infants on time and patience. Presentation of motherhood through the mass media, especially television, does little to bring home the realities. It is hardly surprising that the study by Brown and others referred to earlier, found:

Working-class women in the early stages of rearing their families are doubly at risk: first because they experience more severe events and major difficulties than a comparable middle-class group and secondly because the quality of their marriage is, at this stage, on the whole, poor.[28]

Brown's work would seem to indicate the following sequence of events.

1. Wives, especially working-class wives, see motherhood as the great goal in their lives, and set themselves unrealistic expectations in this event.

2. At the birth of the first child, the husband fails to maintain the interests he shared with his wife, and loses interest in her. (In addition, he may be jealous of the baby.)

3. Marriage partners constantly reaffirm one another's identity by redefining reality for one another through the discussion of the events of their lives.[29] This process suffers from attrition following childbirth; the wife is isolated from her husband, feels a decreasing sense of her own worth, a lowering self-esteem, and this feeling indicates a lower threshold for symptoms of neurotic disability.

Childbirth itself is an obviously stressful event. One study describing some of the difficulties faced by mothers has been mentioned.[30] Other studies have been made showing a rise in rates of hospitalisation for psychiatric reasons at about this time.[31] However, it is difficult to establish how much such rates are due to the effect of the physical strain of childbearing, how much to the burden put on the mother's social contacts and support systems at the time, and how much to the routine of treating childbearing as a 'sickness' which by itself involves hospitalisation.

Elizabeth Bott has contrasted unfavourably the social situation of the young mother in our society with that of mothers in tribal societies. In modern industrial society, mothers often know very little about babies. During pregnancy they encounter a whole host of medical personnel – general practitioner, antenatal staff, hospital delivery ward staff, hospital maternity ward staff, people at Child Welfare clinics – none of whom have close liaison with one another, and none of whom have any connection with her relatives, neighbours and friends. She may be expected to continue running her home until the very last moment; her husband, probably the only other adult in her household, may be of little use, and will probably be expected to continue with his own job anyway. In the circumstances it is hardly surprising if young women find the onus of motherhood sometimes too much for them.[32] Perceptive personal accounts of the experiences of women as recipients of medical care during pregnancy and childbirth have recently been given by professional sociologists.[33]

The spiralling divorce rate is another pointer to the increasing fragility of family life, and divorce is another change of status which constitutes a threat to mental health. Robert Chester studied the experiences of 150 divorcing women in Hull in the late 1960s. Only 20 of them claimed that their health was unaffected by the divorce. Two thirds had been to see their doctor, mostly in connection with conditions such as 'nerves' or 'depression'. Their symptoms had been particularly marked around the time of their separation from their husbands.[34] The result of divorce is to create one-parent families. Here the preconditions for stress are potentially huge: guilt over the breakdown of the marriage in the surviving parent; lack of support for the surviving parent; difficulties for the children ranging from lack of adults to observe (if the surviving parent lives alone, the children do not hear adults talking to one another in the home unless there are visitors) to lack of a parental model, from whom to learn appropriate sex behaviour for those children of the same sex as the lost parent; and lack of the social status of the child possessing both father and mother.

Clearly, these lacks are not always met in a satisfactory way where a child has both parents, and bad parenting may be positively harmful. But the child with a single parent or of no parents, is likely to have a handicapped start in life in both the psychological and the material sense.

Widows and widowers share many of the problems faced by divorcees. Widowhood is another change of status which can be threatening to mental health: a study of Salford found an inception rate of 534 widows per 100,000 entering psychiatric care, compared with a rate of 321 for married women. The difference between widowers and married men was even more pronounced.[35] However, the harmful effect of widowhood on health goes further. Other studies have reported higher rates than anticipated of physical illness, and even death, among those recently bereaved. Death from 'a broken heart' seems more than just a picturesque phrase.[36] A large investigation of the effect of the death of a parent indicated that this appeared to be a stressful event which led to psychiatric breakdown in some individuals; depression in adults appears especially likely to follow the death of the opposite-sex parent.[37]

One group whose mental health problems are virtually ignored are those single people, nearly all of them women, who stay at home to care for elderly or ailing relatives. This group has been largely ignored by all services, not merely the psychiatric ones, and in recent years the National Council for the Single Woman and her Dependants has begun to campaign vigorously on their behalf. While such women can receive the Invalid Care Allowance, this is much less than unemployment benefit, and the N.C.S.W.D. points out that these women are saving public funds twice over by performing the burden of care themselves, and receiving less state support than they would were they registered as unemployed.

The N.C.S.W.D. conducted a survey among its members, finding widespread evidence of financial problems, loneliness and exhaustion among them.[38] While it is impossible to chart the extent of the problem fully the apathy with which these women are regarded throughout our society makes a poignant contrast with the enthusiastic interest shown for the problems of mixed-up teenagers.

The identity crisis

Another problem of family life which manifests itself in ways akin to mental illness is that of a turbulent adolescence. Adolescence is a time of difficulty and trauma, when a young person seeks to establish an identity for himself and break away from the bonds of parents and home. This process has been described in detail by Erikson,[39] who has coined the phrase 'identity crisis' to cover the process of psychological growth during adolescence which involves the assumption of adult status and manners. Erikson points out that technological advances are extending the period between early school life and the young person's final access to specialised work. Adolescence therefore becomes more conscious and long-drawn-out, almost a way of life in itself. The simultaneous pressures to physical intimacy, occupational choice, the experience of competition, and awareness of their own unique individual identity can prove too much for some adolescents to cope with.

Teenage rebellion is now recognised almost as a normal phase of growing up. Many young people who pass through a rebellious phase in adolescence, go on to become sober and conforming adult members of society. It has been pointed out that the inner turmoil of the adolescent is often unnoticed by the adults around him.[40] Yet teenage distress is clearly one facet of the behaviour of the young women described by Laing and Esterson we have mentioned earlier. It is at times difficult to draw the line at the point at which such behaviour crosses the borderline with psychosis. Adolescents are coming to terms with how they are viewed in the eyes of others, as compared to how they feel themselves to be. The views of themselves projected by their immediate family are of course critical. In Laing's families as described in *Sanity, Madness and the Family*, this view contains irreconcilable elements, reflecting unresolved conflicts in the parents' own marriages. As Friedenberg puts it,

The parents take the process of human growth as itself a form of insult which challenges their opportunity to continue making demands on their daughter, that expresses the uneasy truce their marriage has become.[41]

Another useful concept has been based on Lidz's small study of middle- and upper-class families which produced a psychiatric patient from their ranks. Starting with the observation that not all bad marriages produced a child ultimately to be labelled schizophrenic, Lidz distinguished two kinds of pathological relationship among the parents of the patients: 'marital schism' where couples failed to achieve complementarity of purpose, each tried to undermine the other, and to compete for the children's loyalty and affection; and 'marital skew' where one dominant partner is responsible for bringing up the child in a pathological manner, and the other partner passively accepts this situation, making the other appear 'normal' in the eyes of the child.[42]

In a subsequent paper, sex differences are elaborated upon:

Schizophrenic males often came from skewed families with passive ineffectual fathers and disturbed engulfing mothers, whereas schizophrenic girls typically grew up in schismatic families with narcissistic fathers who were often paranoid and, while seductive to the daughter, were disparaging of women, and with mothers who were unempathic and emotionally distant.[43]

While the relevance of this work, based as it is on very small samples, to the total clinical entity of schizophrenia has already been doubted, it does seem that these are interesting insights into family pathology. They do indicate a kind of closed world: certainly much of the in-fighting in families of schizophrenics seems unnecessary and tedious to an uncommitted outsider. The ability of the young person to break the parental bonds would seem a prerequisite (often perhaps the only one needed) to normal social and psychological functioning.

Neurotic processes in the family

Disturbed family relationships are found in the far commoner neurotic conditions, as well as the more spectacular psychotic ones. If a sufficiently wide definition of neurosis is adopted, of course, almost everyone is included. This can be true even at clinical level. As Kellner remarked in his investigation, *Family Ill health*, 'If the investigation went on long enough, almost all the families could be labelled neurotic families.'[44]

What can we say about neurotic processes within intact families? Which family members are most vulnerable? Research has been concentrated on the marriage relationship; given the predominance of females among neurotic patients, the relative lack of interest in mother–daughter relationships is surprising.

Interest in the marriage relationship has grown not simply because of its central place in family life, but because a number of studies have shown that neurosis affects both partners of a marriage more often than would be expected by chance. One careful study, based on men designated neurotic and currently attending for psychiatric out-patient treatment, suggested that the cause of this concordance was more likely to lie in pathogenic interaction rather than assertive mating. In other words, neurotics did not select neurotic partners at marriage; but their partners became neurotic in the course of marriage.[45]

Why this should happen is a question difficult to answer beyond the 'commonsense' level of blaming the difficulties of living with a neurotic partner. What are the mechanisms involved, and over what topics do difficulties arise?

Certainly there is evidence that marriages containing a neurotic partner appear to be less satisfactory to the partners than other marriages.[46] These and other studies[47] suggest that one important area where the partners are in conflict is that of child care.

The features of the marriages principally examined have been dominance, segregation and the giving of mutual affection.

The studies already quoted show an association between neurosis and marriages in which one partner is dominant, in which marital roles are segregated, and where mutual affection appears to be low. They provide a reasonably uniform picture, despite taking experimental samples of neurotics of both sexes, and of differing severity of problem (some used psychiatric out-patients, others G.P.-identified cases). Their limitations must also be mentioned: none used particularly large samples and aspects of relationships such as the giving and accepting of affection are clearly difficult to measure. However, a start has been made, though the kind of investigation to make significant advances in this field would need both experimental rigour and an imaginative approach. We are still some way from achieving deep insights into the nature of neurosis within marriage.

The question of the extent to which neurosis can be said to be handed on by faculty socialisation from one generation to another is an interesting one, which again has not generated the amount of research it might have done. Rycroft's remark, that the literature 'may be searched in vain for a satisfactory or coherent account of the sort of childhood which predisposes to hysteria'[48] can be applied almost equally strongly to other varieties of neurosis. Given the widely-recognised importance of the family setting in the development of personality, this gap is particularly surprising.[49] It contrasts markedly with the concern shown for familial factors in the transmission of schizophrenia discussed earlier.

One feature of family life which has been noted as pathological has been that poor mental health of women is associated with low self-esteem, especially among working-class women. This is apparent both from clinically oriented studies such as Brown's, which has already been mentioned,[50] and more broadly based investigations based on concepts such as anomie or alienation.[51] These studies are dealt with at greater length in the next chapter.

Some family situations are undoubtedly stressful, yet the very ordinariness appears to preclude them from consideration by clinicians and researchers. The experience of coping with an elderly infirm relative, for example, is a common one: it may be becoming commoner. A small study[52] has noted the strain that coping with a senile patient makes on the physical and psychological resources of relatives. The widespread experience of coping with a handicapped child is a much more recent development, with the preservation of life of substantial numbers of handicapped children now possible. The difficulties this imposes on relatives has been documented by a growing number of writers.[53] Indeed it has been suggested that a new medical speciality appears to be arising to study and record the effects on families of caring for a sick relative. These effects include marital strife, breakdown, chronic misery, and loss of income.[54]

Demographic changes in the family

To draw this chapter together, let us consider the demographic changes which have been occurring during this century to alter the shape of families.

1. The expectation of life has gone up some 20 years, from 48 to 68 for men, and 52 to 74 for women.

2. Retirement from working life has occurred earlier. Thus the length of time between retirement and death has increased at both ends.

3. The number of children born to the average married couple has decreased dramatically; child-bearing is finished for many women before their thirtieth birthday, and their dependent children are off their hands while they are still in their forties. (This means that thirty years' life is still ahead of them.)

4. With the increasing length of formal education, people are entering the labour force later.

5. All women enter the labour force, except those who start their family before their formal education is complete. Most aim to return to work once their children start school on a full-time basis.

6. Marriage is extremely popular. Very few people remain unmarried, though this is offset to some extent by those who are temporarily between marriages.

These changes create problems for the following groups:

1. The parents of small children, who as described earlier, form isolated nuclear family units: difficulties arise when the young mother is marooned at home without support for the tasks of child-rearing and when family financial resources may be severely stretched.

2. Older families, where both parents are out at work. Domestic appliances remove some of the burdens of housework, but there is unlikely to be any domestic labour available to cope with crises such as a sick child. Those with sufficient money to house and feed an extra person will be able to recruit an *au pair*.

3. Elderly individuals or couples who become unable to look after themselves. They have had few children who, as indicated above, might be fully committed themselves.

There remain, therefore, within 'the family' relatively few individuals to cope both with the material demands of family life 'providing and caring for dependent members' and to carry the intense emotional load of close family relationships. What is perhaps surprising is not that so many families 'break down', but that the entire family system does not fall apart under the burdens that are imposed upon it.

Currently it has become fashionable in some circles to 'blame' the family for mental illness: certainly it is hardly surprising that given the unfortunate circumstances of early life for some individuals, they subsequently receive the attentions of workers in the mental health field. However, the contemporary family's faults and shortcomings should not blind us to its strengths: perhaps those concerned with mental illness should also look at the families which maintain themselves as loving, coping, functioning groups, and consider how this is possible.

4

MENTAL ILLNESS: A FORM OF SOCIAL DEVIANCE?

Mental illness and social control

Mental illness is essentially the name given to those forms of human behaviour adjudged to fall within the competence of psychiatrists to treat. The limits of this behaviour necessarily vary from culture to culture, as the professional province of the psychiatrist is not always constant in time and place.

Much of the 'advance' of psychiatry has lain, as we have seen earlier, in viewing itself as the humane wing of a humanitarian society. In the name of progress the treatment of the mentally ill has moved from torture to 'expel devils' and 'fight witchcraft' through custodial care to its present emphasis on rehabilitation and on into the future, with a growing concern for preventive measures.

These changes have come about through a variety of pressures: principally on the one hand the growing status and expertise of 'scientific medicine' and on the other a concern for basic human dignity to be available to all. As part of the second movement has come a growing reluctance to deprive people of their freedom, in attempting to keep them out of state custody (whether in prison or forcibly contained within a psychiatric hospital).

Thus, for many convicted of crimes, the label 'mentally ill' offers a more optimistic future than the label 'criminal'. Psychopaths, for example, are now often hospitalised in special units rather than sent to gaol. In other parts of the world, such distinctions are made differently. Psychopaths convicted of offences may be summarily gaoled; or political offenders under totalitarian regimes may be hospitalised as a humane alternative to prison.

The involvement of psychiatrists with the handling of political deviants has been described in Soviet Russia.

The Russian criminal code censures offences against the state more heavily than offences against individuals or private property. Murder does not warrant capital punishment, but property speculation may. Those who wish to assert aggressively their religion, or to attempt reform in the political process, are considered particularly dangerous. Criticism of the state is a major crime.

A comprehensive local psychiatric service exists, which treats mild conditions. The prevalence of schizophrenia in Moscow is double that of British studies: a wider definition is applied by Russian than by British psychiatrists. The label of mental illness can readily be applied to awkward critics. The mentally ill are deemed 'unfit to plead' and court appearances, with their attendant undesirable publicity, are avoided. This outcome can be justified on humanitarian grounds as being a much kinder form of disposal than sending to prison. However, as Lader has pointed out,[1] dissidents are treated in special hospitals which are managed by internal security forces: they are usually former prisons surrounded by barbed wire. Their orderlies are recruited from convicted prisoners taken from the corrective labour institutions. Some of the top psychiatrists are members of the K.G.B.

Lader emphasises that this situation has arisen as a result not merely of the Soviet criminal code, but out of the imprecision of psychiatric diagnoses. Not only is the diagnosis of schizophrenia in Russia based on looser criteria than in Britain (in a similar way to American–British differences mentioned in Chapter 1) but Russian psychiatrists permit diagnoses such as 'creeping schizophrenia' or 'paranoid development of the personality' which would be unlikely to be recognised at all as psychiatric diagnoses in Britain. The ultimate in cynicism is to label those who wish to bring about political reform as suffering from 'reformist delusions', and to incarcerate them as a result.[2]

Of course the psychiatrist acts as gaoler in Britain too. About one psychiatric admission in eight takes place as a result of the exercise of the state's statutory power, though the percentage is falling slowly. Not many years ago the figure was substantially higher. In some particular situations – the role of the psychiatrist responsible for university students, for example – there would appear to be serious potential conflicts between serving the needs of the patients and those of the employer or state institution.[3]

The label that deviant behaviour earns – whether 'criminal', 'mentally ill', 'eccentric' or whatever – is therefore determined to some extent by the culture in which that behaviour occurs. Changes in the epidemiology of mental illness are therefore likely to reflect such differences in definition.

Models of mental illness

Some of the difficulties in defining precisely what constitutes mental illness were set out in Chapter 1. Mention was also made of the typology of 'models of madness' constructed by Siegler and Osmond.[4] This is an appropriate point to consider these models in rather more detail.

The model which is presented as dominant in the discussion of Siegler and Osmond is the medical one. That is, a doctor diagnoses a 'disease' on the basis of his observation of symptoms and the knowledge that he possesses; the patient is exempted from normal responsibilities in assuming the 'sick role' and is expected to collaborate with the doctor's prescribed treatment;[5] the disease will run its anticipated course and the result, it is hoped, will be the cure of the patient and his restoration to normal living.

This is of course the dominant model for medical treatment, and as psychiatry is a branch of medicine this model dominates the treatment of the mentally ill. However, Siegler and Osmond point out that possible confusion arises between the sick role and what they term the 'psych' role of those who are troubled rather than ill, and in search of counsel rather than treatment. They point out too that there are substantial differences between the practice of medicine by an orthodox practitioner with a one-to-one relationship with patients, and a doctor working in a public health or scientific research setting.

Two other models besides the medical one give rise to a partial rather than a total view of madness. They stop short of an attempt at a complete explanation. These other partial models are the moral and the impaired models.

The moral model is one in which the mad person's behaviour is construed as bad, on the basis of judgements made concerning his observed behaviour. Although 'moral treatment' is generally thought of as a nineteenth-century phenomenon in the management of the mentally ill, Siegler and Osmond include the treatment regimes of behaviour therapists under this heading. The impaired model, like the medical model, can be activated when someone appears incapable of doing what a normal person should be capable of; but in the case of the impaired model, social pressures are not brought into play to bring the subject back to normalcy. This is because the subject is seen as handicapped, and unlikely to be restored to normalcy by treatment.

The remaining models are seen as 'continuous', that is offering a total explanation for madness. They are the psychoanalytic model, the social (deprivation) model, the psychedelic model, the family interaction model, and the conspiratorial model.

The psychoanalytic model is derived from Freudian psychoanalysis: it sees an individual's problems as stemming from long-standing emotional difficulties, often going back to early childhood. Treatments are derived from classical psychoanalytical techniques such as free association and the analysis of dreams.

The social model sees mental illness arising out of social disadvantage, the symptom of a 'sick' society. Its solution is seen chiefly through improvements in the social and physical conditions of the lowest strata.

The psychedelic model sees the mad as those who have been 'chosen' by society to act out its problems; with patience, they can reveal themselves as particularly gifted members of society; they must be allowed to develop their potential for inner exploration and to change the world through their insights.

The family interaction model is associated particularly with the work of Laing, and has already been dealt with in Chapter 3.

The conspiratorial model sees madness as stemming from the way the mentally ill are labelled: madness exists in the eye of the beholder. This theory has been particularly associated with the work of Thomas Scheff, who was mentioned in Chapter 1. Evidence in its support can be taken from two very different sources.

Provision for psychiatric hospitalisation in China is relatively poor. A high percentage of the few psychiatric beds are occupied by patients diagnosed as schizophrenic, although the overall incidence of the condition is probably low. Once in hospital, the mentally ill are treated by very humane methods and regimes.[6] Violence, and the threat of violence, are conspicuous by their absence.

A similar atmosphere of gentle concern and relatively weak physical constraint is reported from the Hutterite communites studied by Eaton and Weil.[7] This is in contrast to the general feeling among the lay public in many countries that the mentally ill are to be regarded as dangerous and potentially violent.[8] By *not* treating the mentally ill as people to fear, the Chinese and the Hutterites do not put them into intolerable situations where violent responses are triggered. Eaton and Weil mention the absence of free-floating anxiety among the Hutterites; but it may also be that by the absence of a violent stereotype of mental illness, the Hutterites are able to restrict its manifestation among their members. And the absence of such violent patients may have been responsible for the growth of the view, erroneous in fact, that the Hutterites are free of mental illness.

Mental illness and gender

Mental illness is commoner in women than in men. Sixty-three per cent of psychiatric admissions in 1970 were female. Why should this be so? This deceptively simple question is seldom asked. Yet its implications for the whole area of social deviance are considerable. One study of neurosis in one general practice population[9] concentrated on neurosis in women and found a higher rate for married and widowed women than for single women. But the low rate for single women may have been due to their youth. The study by Shepherd et al. of psychiatric illness in nearly fifty London general practices[10] confirms Tonge's figures of high female attendance throughout the life-cycle. Neurosis, for example, was twice as common in women. Tonge asked if the stress on the female reproductive system might account for high psychiatric consulting rates during child-bearing years, though he noted that figures for psychiatric consultations do not drop in the years following the menopause. Shepherd's study indicates that figures for consulting females actually go up about this time: the rates for women reach a peak of over 200 consulting per 1,000 population at risk for women aged 45 to 64. Shepherd points out that these figures differ from those for psychiatric referral to out-patient clinics, where the peak is usually reported in a younger age-group.

An American writer, surveying the literature on illness and the feminine role, points out the paradox that, although women tend to report more symptoms and use medical services more than men, they tend to live longer.[11] She considers three possible explanations: that it is culturally more acceptable for women to be ill (they are less likely than men to be stigmatised for departing from normal 'adult' roles by, for example, showing their emotions by crying); the sick role is more compatible with other social roles for women than for men (though, as she points out, the evidence here is conflicting); and that the greater strains in women's biological and sexual roles mean that women have more illnesses.

These suggestions are of particular relevance in a consideration of mental illness, though they do not exhaust the possibilities that have been put forward. The writings of feminists in recent years have devoted considerable attention to mental health issues.

Phyllis Chesler[12] discusses several factors which may contribute to a heavy female involvement with psychiatric services. Women express mental illness through a different pattern of symptomatology from that of men. 'Women's' symptoms – typical examples are depression, anxiety, frigidity and suicide attempts – indicate what Szasz has called 'a dread of happiness' which characterises those who are at the mercy of others. Depression rather than aggression is the typical 'female' response to disappointment or loss. Depression may be a way of keeping 'a deadly faith with the feminine role'. Even when aggression is expressed it may be turned inwards: the majority of suicide attempts are by women. Even then, women are more likely to fail: the majority of successful suicides are men.

This inability to achieve autonomy leads Chesler to suggest that perhaps women were the first group in history to be enslaved by another group, men. Women were (and still, residually, are) the prototype slaves.

A further reason for women's high involvement with mental illness is that the culturally-approved helplessness and dependency permits them to fit into the 'career' of the 'mental patient' more easily than men. Once in treatment, patients are encouraged into roles that foster submission, dependency and infantilism.

The attitudes of therapists are likely, Chesler argues, to reinforce these attributes. Most psychiatrists are men. The membership of the American Psychiatric Association was 90 per cent male in the 1960s, and the position is broadly similar in Britain. They treat patients with a double standard, and Chesler quotes several pieces of research to illustrate this.

In one of them, a questionnaire was completed by 79 clinicians (psychiatrists, psychologists and social workers; 46 males and 33 females) who were asked to rate certain bipolar traits as representing healthy male, healthy female, or healthy adult (sex unspecified) behaviour. The results showed that the clinicians held different standards of health for men and women. The concept of a healthy man resembled that of a healthy adult, but that of a healthy woman differed significantly from both. In general, women were described as more submissive, less independent, less adventurous, more easily influenced, less aggressive, less competitive, less objective, more emotional, and so on.

A sample of non-professional subjects indicated that personality traits that were judged as 'socially desirable' correlated very closely with the traits selected by the clinicians as healthy male and healthy adult traits. However, the socially undesirable traits resembled those judged by the clinicians to be characteristic of females.

It seems therefore that the clinicians not only perceived a healthy female as being unlike a healthy adult, but actually possessing characteristics which are widely felt to be undesirable.[13] As Chesler says, 'The ethic of mental health in our society is a masculine one'.[14]

The view of mental patients as typified by dependency and helplessness – typically 'feminine' traits – is widely held, not merely among therapists and their patients, but among theoretical writers too. Indeed, viewing the development of theory in psychiatry it could be said that the anti-feminist theme of 'woman as villain' runs through much of the thinking and writing of influential psychiatrists. Juliet Mitchell opens her book on this theme[15] with the words 'The greater part of the feminist movement has identified Freud as the enemy'; however, her analysis of his writings goes on to make the point that psychoanalysis is not a recommendation for a patriarchal society, but rather an analysis of one. Freud's limitations lay not in his analysis, but that he did not go on to denounce the society in which he performed it.

Feminist denunciations of Freudian psychoanalysis and its subsequent variants have now become something of a commonplace. The interest and controversy generated by Bowlby's concept of maternal deprivation has already been looked at, in Chapter 3. This discussion has done nothing to make life easier for women. Discussions of maternal deprivation must have caused guilt feelings in countless women, but in precious few men.

The writings of Laing and Esterson, like those of Bowlby, follow in the Freudian tradition. Their contribution to our understanding of family processes in schizophrenia has also been discussed in the last chapter. They have also attracted the attention of the feminists, including both Chesler and Mitchell.

The subjects of *Sanity, Madness and the Family* show a disturbing emphasis on the problems of women as investigated by men. They comprise eleven young women, all diagnosed schizophrenic, who were in lay terms facing up to the problems of establishing their identity and moving away from home, and the problems of the parents (especially the mothers) in facing up to this. Despite a claim that *Sanity, Madness and the Family* marks an advance of our understanding of schizophrenic behaviour from looking at particular relationships (e.g. between the patient and a 'schizophrenogenic mother') to looking at a network of relationships within the nuclear family, mothers still show up badly. As Chesler points out, they are depicted as psychologically insecure, sexually repressed, poorly educated and economically dependent; in a word, essentially 'feminine'. They are also extremely peculiar and without doubt poor models for the unfortunate daughters.

The absence of 'normal' controls in Laing and Esterson's work has already been deplored. Comparison in another sense would also have been welcome: would young men find their independence so difficult to achieve? In such bizarre families it is hard to tell.

More empirical work on the question of why mental illness is commoner in women than in men has been conducted in America, and a debate has been carried out on the subject in the pages of the

American Journal of Sociology. Clancy and Gove conducted telephone interviews with 400 Americans in 1970 and concluded that the excess of symptoms reported by females appeared to reflect real differences and was not an artifact of response bias.[16]

This study has been subjected to considerable criticism, especially by the Dohrenwends, who have themselves assembled the findings of some eighty studies of the epidemiology of mental illness.[17] One of their findings (which agrees with earlier work of Gove's) is that the balance of mental illness between the sexes shifted in the Second World War. In the pre-war studies, the rate of mental illness for men tended to be higher than that for women. This position was reversed in the majority of studies done since the war.

It is tempting to suggest therefore that events during the war may have given a greater stability to men in their social roles, and the new challenges facing women (most especially, moving into jobs in great numbers) has caused this shift. However, the Dohrenwends point out that the reasons are unlikely to be as simple as that.

Reported rates of mental illness in studies conducted after the Second World War were much higher generally, probably because a wider definition of 'mental illness' was becoming acceptable among both psychiatrists and laymen. Further, survey techniques were changing. Pre-war studies had tended to use techniques of asking informants to report on the extent of mental illness among local groups. This would reveal 'publicly known' cases, but would be much less likely to bring to light problems which were essentially 'private'. This became much more likely with the innovations of community surveys after the war which asked for the self-reporting of health of whole populations. Thus a wider revelation of 'private' problems occurred: this accounts both for the upswing in reported 'mental illness' and the fact that more women (who were more likely than men to suffer from 'private' problems) were now appearing as mentally ill.

The other finding of the Dohrenwends is equally important. When the prevalence of mental illness is divided into its major illness categories, there are great differences in the sex distribution. Out of 24 studies of manic-depressive psychosis, for example, 18 have higher rates for women. With neurosis, the ratio is even higher: 28 out of 32. There are no consistent sex differences revealed in 34 studies of functional psychosis, nor in the 26 of these that deal with schizophrenia separately. However, 22 of the 26 studies of personality disorder report higher rates for men.

These findings strengthen the point that discussion based on mental illness as if it were a single entity is potentially misleading.

However, the overall impression that mental illness does afflict more women than men is a very strong one, and is borne out by considering mental illness at most levels of severity. Our understanding can be furthered if we contrast the 'deviant' role of the mentally ill with the 'deviant' role of the criminal. To some extent they complement on another: as a majority of the mentally ill are women, a majority of criminals are men. As Smart has pointed out, there is a frequently-made assumption that women offenders are seen as 'sick' by the English penal system.[18] The Dohrenwends have documented how patterns of psychiatric diagnosis differ for men and women.[19] Smart suggests how this might come about: men, whose cultural role is less expressive, are therefore given more socially visible diagnoses such as alcoholism and personality disorder, and are under-represented in the more expressive or private conditions such as depression or neurosis. She suggests, echoing Chesler, that it is the untenable nature of the traditional female role which produces the higher incidence of breakdown amongst women.

Mental illness and social inequality

A second major feature of the epidemiology of mental illness concerns its over-representation among those who are lowly in the social scale. Here the patterns for each psychiatric diagnosis varies, and what must not be forgotten is that the referral patterns also vary by class.

The diagnosis of 'psychopath' or 'schizophrenic' or 'sufferer from personality disorder' is only made after what might be a fairly lengthy interchange of information and opinions among the patient, his relatives, doctors or social workers, and quite possibly the police, and the courts. Hollingshead and Redlich[20] have noted that upper-class patients are more likely to arrive at a psychiatrist via a simple process of self-referral, or with pressure from a relative; lower-class patients, on the contrary, may have experienced the greater pressures from society's figures of authority. Indeed, they might see mental hospital, as did the hero of Kesey's *One Flew Over the Cuckoo's Nest*, as a soft option if it can be negotiated in the place of a prison sentence.

Yet it is still probable that irrespective of the technique of referral, the genuine incidence of mental illnesses is higher among lower social classes. Why should this be so? Precise answers are clearly not possible: it may be that genetic factors are associated with lower levels of intelligence, physical health and emotional stamina, as one descends the social scale. However, it is certain that constraint and stress are much more a part of lower-class than upper-class life, in that choices with respect to jobs, spending and leisure patterns are that much more restricted. The simple task of bringing up a family on low wages or an unemployment benefit creates obvious problems on psychological as well as material levels. The boost to morale that comes from being able to spend a little on extravagances after a long period watching every penny is widely acknowledged. The rich, who can exercise such choice every day, are not subject to this constraint. In one sense, they can be thought of as being able to 'buy' cures, though wealth in itself does not of course provide a guard against emotional troubles like feelings of worthlessness as a person or a lack of pattern or meaning in life.

The association of low social class position with various psychiatric diagnoses has already been mentioned in Chapter 2. It must be remembered that the problems of those in low social class position are not simply those of shortage of money. In our materialist and competitive society shortage of money, and of status, can produce a loss of self-esteem. The American sociologist John Scanzoni has documented the relatively low self-esteem felt by the wives of manual workers.[21] George Brown's study[22] of depressed women in London reached similar conclusions.

Studies of those at the bottom of the pile have been numerous – Rutter and Madge[23] have reviewed thoroughly the voluminous literature on the 'cycle of disadvantage' – but few researchers have given clear insights into how lives have been organised to come to terms with relative failure, except in isolated instances. Undoubtedly the higher rates for mental illness among the lower classes bear witness to this problem.

The association of poor physical health with low social class has been frequently demonstrated, and the reasons for this may resemble those in the mental health field. Relatively speaking, working-class people have a poorer knowledge of the health services, how to approach them and what to expect of them. This is particularly true of psychiatry, where approaches may be inhibited further by the known association of mental health personnel with direct agencies of social control, the law courts and the police. Further, the 'performance' of lower-class patients is likely to be affected adversely by their expectations of therapists taking an active lead in directing treatment, and by their comparatively passive approach themselves to the patient role. When this is combined with poor verbal ability it is likely that psycho-therapeutic treatment regimes will fail.

It may even be no exaggeration to suggest that class is associated with different attitudes to the body. American sociologists have suggested that whereas middle-class people think of their bodies as machines to be preserved and kept in perfect functioning condition, working-class people view them as having a limited span of utility: to be enjoyed in youth and then to suffer deterioration with age.[24] Perhaps it is the acceptance of earlier physical wear-and-tear on working-class bodies that is the real class discriminator: the result of poor diet and more smoking as well as harsher working conditions.

Other features of lower-class life act as inhibitors of mental health: an inability to control one's destiny, and the socialisation processes of lower-class family life.

The inability to control one's destiny manifests itself in employment and housing, to take just two major examples. The job choice of the unskilled is more circumscribed than among any other group in the work force. Security of employment is also poor. For many, especially at times of general economic insecurity, jobs may materialise and disappear as if by magic.

Similarly the allocation of housing to intending council tenants often proceeds in a way which the people concerned fail to understand; once in the council sector, many tenants find themselves in the iron grip of a rule-book which constrains how they use their home, what colour they paint it, what pets they can keep, and so on. Both jobs and housing are distributed through impersonal agencies which lower-class people feel incapable of influencing. It is perhaps surprising that 'working-class paranoia' has not reached the status of a clinical entity.

The socialisation process of the lower classes is reflected in their dominant institution in the work situation: the trade union. Lower-class children experience a socialisation process designed to permit solidarity and discourage competitive striving. Individual enterprise, and thus material success, are discouraged, inhibiting the fullest use of educational opportunity. The class differential in educational achievement has been documented sufficiently frequently not to need further reiteration here. There is of course a growing awareness among the young of all class backgrounds of the harsher features of the 'rat race', but it is notable that those who 'drop out' of the competitive society are drawn disproportionately from higher-class backgrounds. Lower-class young people have so far found the material benefits of a consumer society too far out of reach consciously to reject them.

Mental illness and social change

One of the most striking features of contemporary society is its acceptance of change, both technological and social. This means life has truly become like the river into which, as the Greek philosopher commented, it is impossible to step twice at the same place. All is flux. The continuous rate of change means that the values which underlie behaviour are constantly subject to revision.

Two examples – our attitudes to sex and work – are illustrations of this process.

One reason for justifying forbidding sex outside marriage has always been the fear of unwanted pregnancies, bringing into the world children who would lack a definable legal and social position. Now, with the availability of efficient and aesthetically acceptable techniques of birth control, this argument no longer holds. In the relaxing codes of sexual behaviour, this threat can be ignored. Of course, other arguments still apply to prevent indiscriminate sexual activity: religious belief, fear of venereal disease, and the need to link sexual behaviour with meaningful interpersonal relationships, or at the very least, to ensure that none of the participants suffer psychological harm. But to forbid sexual intercourse for the unmarried on the simple grounds that unwanted babies may be produced no longer holds good. More sophisticated arguments must be produced: of course, the question of the less than universal use of efficient birth control techniques among those not wishing to conceive still remains, and it raises quite separate problems.

Similar major changes affect our attitudes to work. Hard physical work has been considered the lot of men (and women) since before history or the Bible were written. Industrial capitalism was able to take over this work ethic that had endured for many centuries, and harness it in the mines and factories of the nineteenth century. Its virtues – hard work, application, perseverence – became the bedrocks of the industrialised labour force, as they had always served agriculture. Yet conflict rapidly grew, as more and more machines were built which *replaced* the work of men. The labourer became redundant, but instead of joy at his liberation, he felt panic at the imminent fate of starvation for himself and his dependants. In contemporary society the goal stretches before us of redundancies of workers on a massive scale: but we regard the prospect with fear and often try to prevent it, where we should do all we can to bring it about. In Britain there have been dramatic declines in the numbers of people involved in dirty, dangerous, repetitive work like coal-mining. The working week has grown shorter for almost everyone. The economy calls for more and more flexibility from workers; they must learn new skills, re-training in mid-career is becoming a commonplace event. More and more leisure hours have to be filled.

New values are therefore demanded. Hard work, industrial skills acquired with long training, and loyalty to particular employers, though not useless, need less emphasis than adaptability and enterprise. And satisfying ways of filling the longer leisure hours must be found for workers now not so likely to be physically exhausted by many hours of heavy labour.

Such changes are hard to accept. As Eric Hoffer has written, 'No one really likes the new. We are afraid of it.' Every radical adjustment is a crisis in self-esteem; training gives not only the competence to perform a task, but confidence as a person too. Populations undergoing drastic changes are populations of misfits;

where populations subject to drastic changes find only limited opportunities for action, they will substitute faith and pride for self-confidence and self-esteem.[25]

The twentieth century has been a time of rapid and continuous change in all the industrialised nations, even those like Britain which possess extraordinarily stable social structures. The pace of change is such that pressures are hard to bear, especially for the elderly. The climactic events of this century – two world wars, the decline of European imperialism, and the Great Depression – are likely to have left great traumas on the minds of those who have lived through them. Unfortunately, the values that proved vital for survival in those times of difficulty may prove quite unsuitable, harmful even, for coping with the social and economic challenges of the last quarter of this century.

In a similar way, the values surrounding the phenomenon of mental illness, among both patients and healers, have been subject to change. The role of the psychiatrist, for example, has shifted away from a key-keeping function in closed psychiatric hospitals to that of team leader and adviser of professional 'befrienders' of disturbed and unhappy people who are kept out of hospital as much as possible. The role of the other professional workers in the psychiatric health care team – nurses, social workers, and so on – has shifted accordingly.

The perception among patients and the general public of the mentally ill also appears to be changing. Patients are increasingly gaining the confidence to organise themselves, and to obtain spokesmen in positions of power and influence. What has been happening to the lay public's perception is hard to tell, but there are optimistic signs of change for the better.

Very little work on the subject of popular attitudes to mental illness has been done in Britain. One small study in the 1950s found that the picture of a mentally ill person held most generally was that of an unpredictable, deluded, withdrawn 'madman'. Perception of neurotic illness was much less marked.[26] A more recent study of a Scottish urban population was rather more optimistic, with a willingness shown to discuss the subject frankly. Many of the old stereotypes were still around, however: 15 per cent considered masturbation a cause of mental illness.[27] Even this may be taken as a sign of progress, however: in an American sample interviewed in the early 1950s, the figure was 40 per cent. All the more distressing is the fact that this earlier sample was composed entirely of people who themselves worked in a mental hospital.[28] A more recent study of mental hospital employees has pointed out the great variety of orientations towards the mentally ill among different occupational groups.[29]

These studies were among several conducted in America in the 1950s, some of which are reviewed by King.[30] The lay image of mental illness they reveal is that psychotic, rather than neurotic, states are recognised. The features which depict the mentally ill most vividly are those of irrationality, a lack of self-control, and unpredictability. Mental illness is viewed crucially as a departure from normalcy.

A rather more encouraging trend is shown by a series of studies which has made use of a set of case vignettes which have been presented to a variety of samples. These vignettes have presented details of typically mental patients: a paranoid schizophrenic, a simple schizophrenic, a chronically anxious neurotic, a compulsive phobic, an alcoholic and a child with a behaviour disorder. In the two studies in which they were used in the early 1950s, the only case recognised as being mentally ill by a majority of the sample was the paranoid schizophrenic. However, in a series of studies in the 1960s, the numbers recognising this case as one of mental illness went up from around 70 per cent to between 89 and 100 per cent. A majority of those sampled in the 1960s also considered the simple schizophrenic and the alcoholic as mentally ill; compared with some 20 to 30 per cent in the earlier studies. The numbers recognising the other three conditions as mentally ill also showed substantial increases over time.[31]

Crocetti also presents data on social distance and the mentally ill. Fourteen studies are considered and here no clear picture emerges. Although the studies cover a period of 20 years from 1950 to 1970, there is no evidence from this data of growing acceptance of the mentally ill.

Indeed there is considerable hostility to the mentally ill in most intimate relationships. Although between 71 and 93 per cent of the samples questioned said they would accept someone who has been mentally ill as a workmate, the figures for room-mate, which were

79 per cent in Crocetti's own 1970 sample, were above 60 per cent in only two other studies and as low as 23 per cent in one large sample in New York in 1963. Figures for accepting someone who has been mentally ill as a relative or lover were even lower. Only two of the other six samples give a figure higher than Crocetti's 64 per cent for those able to imagine themselves falling in love with someone who has been mentally ill. The numbers of those willing to accept those who have been mentally ill as a relative are lowest of all: over half the studies quoted give a figure of under 30 per cent.[32]

Of course knowledge and attitudes concerning mental illness are not uniform throughout the lay public. Many of the studies that have been made show that younger people, and the better educated, view the mentally ill in a more favourable light.[33] It is also possible that exposure to people who have themselves suffered from mental illness will lead to a more tolerant attitude. A major study in a small Canadian town failed in an attempt to educate the population towards a greater tolerance of the mentally ill,[34] though a recent re-study of the same town[35] indicated some small signs of improvement and another investigation in a small Canadian town[36] revealed more accepting attitudes to the mentally ill. Cohen and Struening[37] point out that the message 'mental patients are poor unfortunates whom we should help out of simple human kindness' might, despite its condescending sound, have proved more effective in changing lay ideas than that of mental patients differing from 'ordinary people' only in degree.

It is curious that another study by Woodward,[38] conducted in the same year (1950) as that of the Cummings, also concerning popularly-held opinions concerning mental illness, and achieving similar results, has received much less attention. Woodward's interpretation of his findings was an optimistic one, suggesting that changes in popular opinions about mental illness were occurring rapidly. Crocetti suggests that the greater interest in the Cummings' work has taken place because their views fit more easily into the portrayal of the mentally ill as social deviants, a view held by many social scientists.

This is a view, Crocetti claims, which is more often based on inference than facts.

There is an attractive and even elegant simplicity in the conceptualisation.

At one stroke the difficult and confusing miscellany of psychiatric diagnostic categories is eliminated; etiological perplexities are at least partially resolved; and complex typologies of deviant behaviour are avoided.[39]

King suggests a number of reasons from within the mental health field itself which should lead to a more tolerant attitude: a growing orientation within hospitals away from 'chronicity' and towards discharging patients; more psychiatric input into the training of doctors; accelerated research; and the growing use of volunteers. However, perhaps the most hopeful sign is the greater acceptance and reduced fear of mental illness among the young and better educated. The question of how such improvements can be fostered further is open to question: as King and others have pointed out, the large number of slang words concerned with mental illness are an indication of how uneasy our society is in coping with it.[40]

Another way of looking at changes in attitudes to mental illness is simply to look at the architecture that is used. It has been felt in the past that mentally ill people need to be shut away in special buildings, 'asylums', and when these were built in significant numbers, two features of their construction were stressed; they were 'safe' – that is, inmates could not get out (many of them being held under statutory powers) – and they were built well away from city centres. Though this was justifiable on various grounds, one of the results was that contact between the inmate and his friends and relatives outside was far from easy. In many cases, hospitalisation meant incarceration. To this extent, mentally ill people were equated with the mentally defective and the inhabitants of the workhouse.

Of course, attitudes have changed, and those concerning hospitalisation for mental illness in particular. Unfortunately, in many cases the buildings are still with us, and prove highly unsuitable for the new kinds of patients and the new kinds of treatment. Instead of huge buildings located beyond city limits, the mentally ill need a variety of much smaller buildings, either within existing general hospitals or in specialist locations. And with goals of informal entry, day care and preventive measures, services must be provided which guarantee accessibility for the population most at risk: currently those living in urban areas.

Mental illness and sociology

How can sociology contribute towards our understanding of mental illness? In two ways: by considering mental illness as a social construct, and by examining how it is defined and 'acted out' by those involved, both patients and healers. Patients are represented both in terms of the individuals themselves, and in those voluntary groups concerned with their status and welfare. Healers can be clearly identified through their professional statuses. One point about the relationship of patients must be made: that their definition of mental illness, and the norms and values that are associated with it, do not always correspond. The pragmatics of the situation ensure, of course, that it is the healers' views which are generally accepted as valid by the wider society. To some extent, the activities of MIND have in recent years redressed this balance.

The second way sociology can contribute is by looking at those social factors involved in the process by which an individual becomes labelled 'mentally ill', and what happens to him thereafter.

What seems crucial to an individual in enabling him or her to avoid mental illness is success in achieving some kind of satisfaction and happiness in the key roles of life in modern society: as a child in a family and at school; as a worker; as a marriage partner; and as a parent. Severe problems of failure in any of these is likely to lead to stress, tension and instability. Some individuals have the necessary resources to cope; some will find success in one area of life will compensate for disasters elsewhere. But for many the breakdown of one of these key roles will produce the symptoms of 'mental illness' and the subsequent 'career' of a patient. And although stigmatisation of the mentally ill is now far less marked than even a few years ago, the needs of treatment (especially if hospitalisation is involved) are likely to create further social problems.

It is a point made repeatedly in this book that the pattern of mental illness has changed markedly in the past, even in the last few years. More changes in the future are inevitable.

The ideologies that psychiatrists bring to their job, for example, are extremely varied, as we saw in Chapter 1, and this reflects the varied explanations of mental illness that are currently accepted. Already the impact of social science thinking on medical education has been considerable. So too have the advances in chemotherapy which have brought about reductions in the expression of the symptoms of mental illness. It is hardly likely that this situation will remain unaltered for long.

As a reflection of changing ideologies, the organisation of services for the mentally ill is also likely to change. The move away from hospitalisation will almost certainly continue, and periods of hospital treatment become briefer. Emphasis on voluntary treatment and care within the community will almost certainly grow.

The need for greater flexibility and mobility of the working population in terms of changes in the economic structure has already been mentioned. Unemployment is a cause of stress in many families, in terms of both a reduction in living standards and a blow to the prestige of the wage-earner. For young people leaving school and finding no jobs available, there is a likelihood of feelings of frustration and uselessness, and greater opportunities for delinquency and vandalism. As a general rule, it is those already disadvantaged in the acquisition of work skills who are most prone to unemployment.

A second major area where change is likely is in attitudes to marriage and family relationships. The proportion of weddings held in Anglican churches has declined every year that figures have been collected, and in the 1970s the drop has been dramatic. More secular weddings indicate a more secular attitude to the marriage relationship, and growing impatience with failed marriages and a quicker resort to divorce are trends which are unlikely to alter. We may witness pressure to make marriage itself a more flexible affair, with the offer of a variety of contracts, and legal distinctions made between those marriages which produce children and those which do not.

The importance of the extended family has been reduced in certain well-defined ways. (The ways in which its importance has persisted have perhaps received less attention.) The experiences of growing up with just one parent, or with a step-parent, is rapidly becoming the experience of a very large number of children.

The nature of parenting has changed enormously, and such changes are unlikely to freeze at any one point in time. Some of the functions of parents have undoubtedly been lost[41] and some have been taken over by impersonal agencies of the state. For the deserted mother of small children, living at considerable distance from her own kin network, there is often little option but for her and her children to become clients of the state for financial support as they are already for education and health services.

Yet we may see a swing back towards the extended family, as there have been indications of a move back to self-sufficiency in an economic sense among people who resent the growing influence of large organisations on daily life. The economic and material advances of industrialisation have been achieved only at a cost of the loss of tribal warmth. People in industrial society are protected against cold and hunger, but the cost can be loneliness, alienation, and the reliance for meaning and dignity in their private lives on a few fragile relationships. When these fail, mental illness can often be the result.

REFERENCES AND
FURTHER READING

Chapter 1 What is mental illness?

1. A. Crowcroft, *The Psychotic: understanding madness*, Penguin, 1975, p. 35.
2. A. R. K. Mitchell, *Schizophrenia: the meaning of madness*, Priory Press, 1972.
3. D. Bannister, 'The logical requirements of research into schizophrenia', *B. J. Psychiatry*, **114**, (1968).
4. T. S. Szasz, 'Schizophrenia: the sacred symbol of psychiatry', *B. J. Psychiatry*, **129**, (October 1976).
5. B. M. Braginsky et al., *Methods of Madness: the mental hospital as a last resort*, Holt Rinehart, 1969.
6. M. Roth, 'Schizophrenia and the theories of Thomas Szasz', *B. J. Psychiatry*, **129**, (October 1976).
7. R. E. Kendell, *The Role of Diagnosis in Psychiatry*, Blackwell, 1975.
8. A. R. K. Mitchell, op. cit., p. 49.
9. 'Anti-psychiatry: a debate', *The New Left Review*, (1977).
10. D. R. Davis, *Introduction to Psychopathology*, 3rd edn, Cambridge University Press, 1972.
11. D. J. Jolley and T. Arie, 'Organisation of Psychogeriatric Services', *B. J. Psychiatry*, **132**, (1978) 1–11.
12. R. E. Kendell, *The Classification of Depressive Illnesses*, Oxford University Press, 1968.
13. For example by M. Shepherd et al., *Psychiatric Illness in General Practice*, Oxford University Press, 1966; M. R. Eastwood and M. H. Trevelyan, 'Relationship between physical and psychological disorder', *Psychological Medicine*, **2** (1972) 4.
14. See especially T. S. Szasz, *The Myth of Mental Illness*, Harper & Row, 1961; Secker and Warburg, 1962.
15. See especially R. D. Laing, *The Politics of Experience*, Penguin, 1967. For two very different accounts of a journey through breakdown guided on Laingian lines, see D. Reed, *Anna*, Secker and Warburg, 1976; Penguin, 1977; and M. Barnes and J. Berke, *Mary Barnes: two accounts of a journey through madness*, Penguin, 1973.
16. 'Anti-psychiatry: A Debate', *The New Left Review*, (1977) 9.
17. Op. cit., p. 20.
18. G. Baruch and A. Treacher, *Psychiatry Observed*, Routledge and Kegan Paul, 1978.
19. W. Glasser, *Reality Therapy*, Harper and Row, 1965, p. 46.
20. E. Goffman, *Asylums*, Doubleday, 1961; Penguin, 1968.

21. T. J. Scheff, *Being Mentally Ill*, Weidenfeld and Nicholson, 1966, p. 82.
22. W. Gove, 'Societal reaction as an explanation of mental illness: an evaluation', *American Sociological Review*, **35**, 5 (1970).
23. T. J. Scheff (ed.), *Labeling Madness*, Prentice-Hall, 1975, p. 23.
24. M. Siegler and H. Osmond, *Models of Madness, Models of Medicine*, Harper and Row, 1976.
25. *Health and Personal Social Services Statistics, 1976*, HMSO, 1977, Table 9.1, p. 144.
26. *The Facilities and Services of Mental Illness and Mental Handicap Hospitals in England, 1975*, DHSS Statistical and Research Report Series No. 19, HMSO, 1977, Table 1, p. 3.
27. J. A. Grimes, 'The probability of admission to a mental illness hospital or unit', in *In-patient Statistics from the Mental Health Enquiry for England 1975*, DHSS Statistical and Research Report Series No. 20, HMSO, 1978; see also *Health Trends*, **10**, 1, (1978).
28. T. J. Scheff, *Being Mentally Ill*, op. cit.
29. Office of Population Censuses and Surveys, Royal College of General Practitioners, and DHSS, *Morbidity Statistics from General Practice: second national study 1970–1*, Studies on Medical and Population Subjects No. 26, HMSO, 1974.
30. OPCS, Royal College of General Practioners, and DHSS, op cit.
31. M. Shepherd et al, *Psychiatric Illness in General Practice*, Oxford University Press, 1966.
32. R. M. Mowbray et al., 'The General Practitioner's attitude to Psychiatry', *Scot. Med. J.*, **6**, (1961).
33. D. Hicks, *Primary Health Care: a review*, HMSO, 1976, Ch. 13.
34. B. P. and B. S. Dohrenwend, *Social Status and Psychological Disorder*, Wiley, 1969, Table 2.1.
35. D. C. Leighton et al., *The Character of Danger*, Basic Books, 1963.
36. T. S. Langner and S. T. Michael, *Life-Stress and Mental Health*, Free Press, 1963, Table 4.1, p. 76.
37. M. Wadsworth et al., *Health and Sickness: the Choice of Treatment*, Tavistock, 1971.
38. G. Gurin et al., *Americans View their Mental Health*, Basic Books, 1960.
39. J. W. Eaton and R. J. Weil, *Culture and Mental Disorders*, Free Press, 1955.
40. D. C. Leighton and C. Kluckholn, *Children of the People*, Harvard University Press, 1947.
41. A. H. Leighton et al., *Psychiatric Disorder Among the Yoruba*, Cornell University Press, 1963, p. 274.
42. A. Kiev, *Transcultural Psychiatry*, Free Press, 1972; also Penguin, 1972.
43. L. Srole et al., *Mental Health in the Metropolis: the Midtown Manhattan Study*, Vol. 1, McGraw-Hill, 1961, Table 8.4, p. 147.
44. B. J. Ennis and T. R. Litwach, 'Psychiatry and the presumption of expertise: flipping coins in the court room', *California Law Review*, **62** (1974).
45. R. R. Grinker et al., *The Phenomena of Depressions*, Hoeber, 1961.
46. T. K. Temerlin, 'Suggestion effects in psychiatric diagnosis', *J. Nervous and Mental Diseases*, **47** (1968). Reprinted in T. J. Scheff (ed.) *Labeling Madness*, Prentice-Hall, 1975.
47. D. L. Rosenhan, 'On being sane in insane places', *Science*, **179** (1973) 250–58.
48. T. J. Scheff, *Labeling Madness*, op. cit.
49. E. Zigler and L. Phillips, 'Psychiatric diagnosis and symptomatology', *J. Abnormal and Social Psychology*, **63** (1961) 69–75.

50. J. E. Helzer et al., 'Reliability of psychiatric diagnosis, I. A Methodological review', *Archives of General Psychiatry*, **34** 2 (1977) 129–33.

51. J. E. Helzer et al., 'Reliability of Psychiatric Diagnosis II. The test/retest reliability of diagnostic classification', *Archives of General Psychiatry*, **34** 2 (1977) 136–41.

52. J. K. Wing et al., *The Measurement and Classification of Psychiatric Symptoms*, Cambridge University Press, 1974.

53. D. Goldberg, *Detection of Psychiatric Illness by Questionnaire*, Oxford University Press, 1972; D. Goldberg and N. Kessel, 'Psychiatric research in general practice' in *Methods of Psychiatric Research*, eds P. Sainsbury and N. Kreitman, Oxford University Press, 2nd edn, 1975.

54. J. E. Cooper et al., *Psychiatric Diagnosis in New York and London*, Oxford University Press, 1972.

55. B. P. and B. S. Dohrenwend, op. cit., Ch. 7.

56. For the history of psychiatry, see R. Hunter and I. Macalpine, *Three Hundred Years of Psychiatry, 1535–1860*, Oxford University Press, 1963; W. Bromberg, *The Mind of Man*, Harper, 1959; F. G. Alexander and S. T. Selesnick, *The History of Psychiatry*, Allen and Unwin, 1967; E. H. Ackerknecht, A Short History of Psychiatry, Hafner, 2nd edn, 1968.

57. For a detailed account of the development of mental health services see K. Jones, *History of the Mental Health Services*, Routledge and Kegan Paul, 1972.

58. I. Macalpine and R. Hunter, *George III and the Mad-Business*, Allen Lane, 1969.

59. V. Skultans, *Madness and Morals: Ideas on Insanity in the Nineteenth Century*, Routledge and Kegan Paul, 1975.

60. K. Jones, op. cit., Ch. 3.

61. A. W. Clare, *Psychiatry in Dissent*, Ch. 9, Tavistock, 1976.

62. A. A. Rogow, *The Psychiatrists*, Allen and Unwin, 1971.

63. W. E. Henry et al., *The Fifth Profession: Becoming a Psychotherapist*, Jossey-Bass, 1971.

64. D. Viscott, *The Making of a Psychiatrist*, Allison and Busby, 1973.

65. A. Storr, reviewing A. W. Clare's *Psychiatry in Dissent* in *Sunday Times* (6 June 1976).

66. A. A. Rogow, op. cit., pp. 49–50.

67. A. B. Hollingshead and F. C. Redlich, *Social Class and Mental Illness*, Wiley, 1958, p. 156.

68. N. Kreitman, 'Psychiatric orientation: a study of attitudes among psychiatrists', *J. Mental Science*, **108** (1962) 317–28.

69. H. J. Walton and J. Drewery, 'Psychiatrists as teachers in Medical Schools', *B. J. Psychiatry*, **112** (1966) 839–46.

70. D. J. Pallis and B. E. Stoffelmayer, 'Social attitudes and treatment orientation among psychiatrists', *B. J. Medical Psychology*, **46** (1973) 75–81.

71. A. L. Strauss et al., *Psychiatric Ideologies and Institutions*, Free Press, 1964.

72. Op. cit., p. 88.

73. Op. cit., p. 155.

74. T. S. Szasz, 'The Psychiatrist as Double Agent', in A. L. Strauss (ed.), *Where Medicine Fails*, Aldine, 1970.

75. A. L. Strauss et al., op. cit.; W. E. Henry et al., op. cit.; M. North, *The Secular Priests*, Allen and Unwin, 1972; W. E. Henry et al., *Public and Private Lives of Psychotherapists*, Jossey-Bass, 1973; N. Goldie, *Professional Processes among three occupational groups within the mental health field*, Ph. D. thesis, City

University, London, 1974; P. Halmos, *The Faith of the Counsellors*, Constable, 2nd edn, 1977.

76. A development in recent years has been the involvement of volunteers in caring for the mentally ill. See F. Sobey, *The Non-professional Revolution in Mental Health*, Columbia University Press, 1970.

77. B. Wilson, *Religious Sects*, Weidenfeld and Nicholson, 1970. See also R. Wallis, *The Road to Total Freedom*, Heinemann, 1976; and 'Scientology: therapeutic cult to religious sect', *Sociology*, **9** 1 (1975).

78. M. Barnett, *People Not Psychiatry*, Allen and Unwin, 1973.

79. H. A. Lyons, 'Psychiatric sequelae of the Belfast riots', *B. J. Psychiatry*, **118** (1971).

80. M. Fraser, *Children in Conflict*, Secker and Warburg, 1973; also Penguin, 1974.

81. H. A. Lyons, 'Depressive illness and aggression in Belfast', *B. M. J.*, 1 (1972) 342–4.

82. P. Sainsbury, *Recent Developments in Affective Disorders* (ed. A. Coppen and A. Walk), Royal Medico-Psychological Association, 1968.

83. E. Durkheim, *Suicide*, Routledge and Kegan Paul, 1952 (first published 1897).

Chapter 2 Mental illness and social structure

1. B. P. and B. S. Dohrenwend, *Social Status and Psychological Disorder*, Wiley, 1969. A personal account of the contemporary Chinese psychiatric scene, emphasising the low incidence of mental illness, and the enlightened therapy regimes, is to be found in S. S. Kety, 'Psychiatric concepts and treatment in China', *China Quarterly*, **66** (1976).

2. R. E. L. Faris and H. W. Dunham, *Mental Disorders in Urban Areas*, Chicago University Press, 1939.

3. *Mental Health of East London*, 1966; *Mental Illness in Four London Boroughs*, 1969; *Mental Illness in City and Suburb*, 1970.

4. E. H. Hare, 'Mental illness and social conditions in Bristol', *J. Mental Science*, **102** 427 (April 1956).

5. For a survey of this and other sociological approaches to crime, see J. B. Mays, *Crime and its Treatment*, 2nd edn, Longman, 1975.

6. H. G. Morgan et al., 'Urban distribution of non-fatal deliberate self-harm', *B. J. Psychiatry*, **126** (1975).

7. I. M. Castle and E. Gittus, 'The distribution of social defects in Liverpool, *Sociological Review*, **5** 1 (1957).

8. C. Bagley et al., 'Social structure and the ecological distribution of mental illness, suicide and delinquency', *Psychological Medicine*, **3** 2 (1973).

9. See R. Frankenberg, *Communities in Britain*, Penguin, 1966, Ch. 8, for a summary of a number of these studies.

10. G. C. M. M'Gonigle and J. Kirby, *Poverty and Public Health*, Gollancz, 1936. A post-war study illustrating the same theme of practical problems which result in ill-health persisting after rehousing is found in two papers by T. Ferguson and M. G. Pettigrew in the *Glasgow Medical Journal* **35** 8 (1954).

11. M. Young and P. Willmott, *Family and Kinship in East London*, Routledge and Kegan Paul, 1957; also Penguin, 1962.

12. The papers most relevant for mental illness are: F. M. Martin et al., 'The incidence of neurosis in a new housing estate', *B. J. Prev. Soc. Med.*, **11** (1957); H. G. Maule and F. M. Martin, 'Social and psychological aspects of

rehousing', *Advancement of Science*, 12 (1956); A. Cartwright and M. Jefferys, 'Married women at work', *B. J. Prev. Soc. Med.*, 12 (1958).

13. E. H. Hare and G. K. Shaw, *Mental Health on a New Housing Estate*, Oxford University Press, 1965. A similar picture of little difference in psychiatric morbidity between a housing estate and a long-established area is reported in R. A. Hardman, 'A comparison of morbidity in two areas', *J. Coll.G. P.*, 9 (1965) 226.

14. Lord Taylor and S. Chave *Mental Health and Environment*, Longman, 1964.

15. R. N. Morris and J. Mogey, *The Sociology of Housing*, Routledge and Kegan Paul, 1965.

16. S. D. Coleman, *Mental Health and Social Adjustment in a Scottish New Town: an exploratory study in East Kilbride*, Institute of Economic and Social Research, Glasgow University, n.d.

17. I. Clout, 'Psychiatric disturbance in a New Town practice', *Lancet*, 31 March 1962.

18. P. Jephcott and H. Robinson, *Homes in High Flats*, Oliver and Boyd, 1971; A. Stevenson et al., *High Living*, Melbourne University Press, 1967.

19. D. M. Fanning, 'Families in flats', *B. M. J.*, 4 (1967).

20. A. R. Gillis, 'High-rise housing and psychological strain', *J. Health Social Behaviour*, 18 (1977).

21. V. Hole, 'Housing in social research', in E. Gittus (ed.), *Key Variables in Social Research*, Vol. 1, Heinemann, 1972.

22. N. C. Moore, 'Psychiatric illness and living in flats', *B. J. Psychiatry*, 125 (1974).

23. N. C. Moore, 'The personality and mental health of flat-dwellers', *B. J. Psychiatry*, 128 (1976) 259–61.

24. E. Gittus, *Flats, Families and the Under-Fives*, Routledge and Kegan Paul, 1976.

25. N. Richman, 'The effects of housing on pre-school children and their mothers', *Dev. Med. Child. Neur.*, 16 (1974).

26. B. Ineichen and D. Hooper, 'Wives' mental health and children's behaviour problems in contrasting residential areas', *Soc. Sci. & Med.*, 8, 6 (1974).

27. O. Newman, *Defensible Space*, Architectural Press, 1972; W. L. Yancey, 'Architecture, interaction and social control: the case of a large-scale housing project', *Environment and Behaviour*, 3 1 (1971).

28. M. Fried, 'Grieving for a lost home', in L. J. Duhl (ed.), *The Urban Condition*, Basic Books, 1963.

29. P. Hall, 'Moving house in the aetiology of psychiatric symptoms', *Proc. Roy. Soc. Med.*, 57 (1964); 'Some clinical aspects of moving house as an apparent precipitant of psychiatric symptoms', *J. Psychosomatic Research*, 10 (1966).

30. S. D. Coleman, op. cit.; F. M. Martin et al., op. cit.

31. D. M. Wilner et al., *Housing, Environment and Family Life*, Johns Hopkins University Press, 1962.

32. D. Hooper et al., 'The health of young families in new housing', *J. Psychosomatic Research*, 16 (1972); N. Richman, op. cit.

33. See especially A. B. Hollingshead and F. C. Redlich, *Social Class and Mental Illness*, Wiley, 1958; and J. K. Myers and B. H. Roberts, *Family and Class Dynamics in Mental Illness*, Wiley, 1959.

34. J. K. Myers and L. L. Bean, *A Decade Later*, Wiley, 1968.

35. B. P. and B. S. Dohrenwend, op. cit.

36. E. J. R. Primrose, *Psychological Illness: a Community Study*, Tavistock, 1962.

101

37. F. Riessman et al., *Mental Health of the Poor*, Free Press, 1964; N. Q. Brill et al., 'Poverty and mental illness: patients' perceptions of poverty as an etiological factor in their illness', *A. J. Psychiatry*, **125** 9 (1961).
38. In addition to the works of the Psychiatric Rehabilitation Association already quoted, see P. McCowen and J. Wilder, *Life-Style of 100 Psychiatric Patients*, Psychiatric Rehabilitation Association, 1975.
39. G. W. Brown et al., 'Social class and psychiatric disturbance among women in an urban population', *Sociology*, **9** 2 (1975).
40. M. Fried, op. cit.
41. See A. Kiev, *Transcultural Psychiatry*, Free Press, 1972; also Penguin, 1972.
42. E. Toker, 'Mental illness in the white and bantu populations in South Africa', *A. J. Psychiatry*, **123** 1 (1966).
43. A. Kiev, 'Psychiatry morbidity of West Indian immigrants in an urban group practice', *B. J. Psychiatry*, **111** (1965).
44. L. K. Hemsi, 'Psychiatric morbidity of West Indian immigrants' *Social Psychiatry*, **2** (1967); G. G. C. Rwegellera, 'Psychiatric morbidity among West Africans and West Indians living in London', *Psychological Medicine*, **7** (1977).
45. For the origin of the term, see W. Watson, 'Social mobility and social class in industrial communities' in M. Gluckman and E. Devons (eds), *Closed Systems and Open Minds*, Oliver and Boyd, 1964.
46. F. Musgrove, *Migratory Elite*, Heinemann, 1963, p. 126. See also B. Jackson and D. Marsden, *Education and the Working Class*, Routledge and Kegan Paul, 1962; Penguin, 1966.
47. J. Tunstall, *The Fishermen*, MacGibbon and Kee, 1962.
48. N. Dennis et al., *Coal is Our Life*, 2nd edn, Tavistock, 1969.
49. A. Kornhauser, *Mental Health of the Industrial Worker*, Wiley, 1965.
50. P. Toynbee, *A Working Life*, Hodder and Stoughton, 1971.
51. V. E. Buck, *Working Under Pressure*, Staples, 1972.
52. W. Freeman, 'Psychiatrists who kill themselves: a study in suicide', *A. J. Psychiatry*, **124** (1967).
53. 'Suicide in doctors' (leading article), *B. M. J.*, **1** (1964) 789–90.
54. D. Marsden and E. Duff, *Workless*, Penguin, 1975, p. 43.
55. H. D. Freeman and O. G. Simmons, *The Mental Patient Comes Home*, Wiley, 1963.
56. O. G. Simmons, *Work and Mental Illness*, Wiley, 1963.
57. O. Odegaard, 'Emigration and insanity', *Acta Psychiatrica* Supplement, **4** (1932); 'Emigration and mental health', *Mental Hygiene*, **20** (1936).
58. A. W. Clare, 'Mental illness in the Irish emigrant', *J. Irish Medical Association*, **57** 1 (1974).
59. A. Kiev, op. cit.
60. L. E. Hinkle and H. G. Wolff, 'Health and the social environment experimental investigations', in A. H. Leighton et al., *Explorations in Social Psychiatry*, Basic Books, 1957.
61. D. Gath et al., *Child Guidance and Delinquency in a London Borough*, Oxford University Press, 1977.
62. M. Power et al., 'Delinquent Schools?', *New Society*, 19 October 1967.
63. A. Clegg and B. Megson, *Children in Distress*, Penguin, 1968.
64. M. W. Susser and W. Watson, *Sociology in Medicine*, 2nd edn Oxford University Press, 1971, p. 210.
65. A. Ryle, *Student Casualities*, Allen Lane, 1969; Penguin, 1973.
66. J. W. Eaton and R. J. Weil, *Culture and Mental Disorders*, Free Press, 1955.

67. J. Spencer, 'The mental health of Jehovah's Witnesses', *B. J. Psychiatry*, **126** (1975).
68. V. Skultans, *Intimacy and Ritual*, Routledge and Kegan Paul, 1974.
69. R. Wallis, *The Road to Total Freedom*, Heinemann, 1976.
70. E. Durkheim, *Suicide*, Routledge and Kegan Paul, 1952, p. 170 (first published 1897).
71. L. Srole et al., *Mental Health in the Metropolis: the Midtown Manhattan Study*, Vol. 1, McGraw-Hill, 1961, Ch. 16.

Chapter 3   Mental illness and the family

1. J. Bowlby, *Maternal Care and Mental Health*, World Health Organisation, 1951.
2. B. Wootton, 'A social scientist's approach to maternal deprivation', in *Deprivation of Maternal Care: a reassessment of its effects*, World Health Organisation, 1962.
3. M. Rutter, *Maternal Deprivation Reassessed*, Penguin, 1972.
4. Ibid., pp. 122–3.
5. R. G. Andry, *Delinquency and Parental Pathology*, Methuen, 1960; D. J. West and D. P. Farringdon, *Who Becomes Delinquent?*, Heinemann, 1973.
6. E. H. Hare and G. K. Shaw, 'Family ill-health', in *B. J. Psychiatry*, **111** (1965).
7. For a survey of the literature, see F. Earls, 'The fathers (not the mothers): their importance and influence with infants and young children', *Psychiatry*, **39** 3 (1976).
8. S. R. Hirsch and J. P. Leff, *Abnormalities in Parents of Schizophrenics*, Oxford University Press, 1975. See also D. R. Davis, 'Family processes in schizophrenia', *B. J. Hospital Medicine*, Nov. (1978).
9. G. Bateson et al., 'Towards a theory of schizophrenia', *Behavioural Science*, **1** 4 (1956).
10. P. Sedgwick, 'R. D. Laing: self, symptom and society', in *Laing and Anti-Psychiatry*, ed. R. Boyers and R. Orrill, Salmagundi, 1971; also Penguin, 1972.
11. P. Lomas, *The Predicament of the Family*, Hogarth Press, 1967.
12. Op cit., p. 15.
13. M. Kohn and J. A. Clausen, 'Parental authority behaviour and schizophrenia', *A. J. Orthopsychiatry*, **26** (1956) 297–313.
14. R. D. Laing and A. Esterson, *Sanity, Madness and the Family*, 2nd edn, Penguin, 1970.
15. M. Siegler and H. Osmond, *Models of Madness, Models of Medicine*, Harper and Row, 1976.
16. A. Collier, *R. D. Laing: The Philosophy and Politics of Psychotherapy*, Harvester Press, 1977.
17. M. Maskin, 'Adaptions of psychoanalytical technique in specific disorders', in J. H. Masserman (ed.), *Science and Psychoanalysis: Vol. III, Psychoanalysis and Human Values*, Grune and Stratton, 1960.
18. E. Z. Friedenberg, *Laing*, Fontana/Collins, 1973.
19. L. C. Wynne and M. T. Singer, 'Thought disorder and family relations of schizophrenics', *Archives of General Psychiatry*, **9** (1963).
20. S. L. Hirsch and J. P. Leff, op. cit., p. 33.
21. L. Wing (ed.), *Early Childhood Autism*, Pergamon, 1976.

22. H. Grunebaum et al., *Mentally Ill Mothers and Their Children*, Chicago University Press, 1974.

23. M. Rutter, *Children of Sick Parents*, Oxford University Press, 1966.

24. M. M. Weissman and E. S. Paykel, *The Depressed Woman*, Chicago University Press, 1974.

25. S. Wolff, *Children Under Stress*, Allen Lane, 1969; Penguin, 1973.

26. P. J. Resnich, 'Child murder by parents: a psychiatric review of filicide', *A. J. Psychiatry*, **126** (1969).

27. S. M. Smith, *The Battered Child Syndrome*, Butterworth, 1975.

28. G. W. Brown et al., 'Social class and psychiatric disturbance among women in an urban population', *Sociology*, **9** 2 (1975) 236.

29. This point is made by P. Berger and H. Kellner, 'Marriage and the construction of reality', *Diogenes*, **46** (1964); reprinted in H. P. Dreitzel (ed.), *Recent Sociology No. 2*, Collier-Macmillan, London, 1970.

30. H. Grunebaum et al., op. cit.

31. C. P. Seager, 'A controlled study of post-partum mental illness', *J. Mental Science*, **106** (1960); T. F. Pugh et al., 'Rates of mental disease related to child-bearing', *New England J. Med.*, **268** (1963); R. S. Paffenbarger, 'Epidemiological aspects of post-partum mental illness', *B. J. Prev. Soc. Med.*, **18** (1964).

32. E. Bott, 'Family and crisis', in *Towards Community Mental Health* (ed. J. D. Sutherland), Tavistock, 1971.

33. J. Comaroff, 'Conflicting paradigms of pregnancy: managing ambiguity in ante-natal encounters', and N. Hart, 'Technology and childbirth: a dialectical autobiography' in *Medical Encounters: The Experience of Illness and Treatment* (A. Davis and G. Horobin eds), Croom Helm, 1977.

34. R. Chester, 'Health and marriage breakdown: experience of a sample of divorced women', *B. J. Prev. Soc. Med.*, **25** (1971).

35. Z. Stein and M. Susser, 'Widowhood and mental illness', *B. J. Prev. Soc. Med.*, **23** 2 (1969) 106.

36. For a review of this field see C. M. Parkes, *Bereavement*, Tavistock, 1972; Penguin, 1975.

37. J. Birtchnell, 'Psychiatric breakdown following recent parent death', *B. J. Medical Psychology*, **48** 4 (1975).

38. National Council for the Single Woman and her Dependants, *Single Women Caring for their Dependants*, July 1978.

39. See especially E. H. Erikson, *Identity: Youth and Crisis*, Faber, 1968.

40. M. Rutter et al., 'Adolescent turmoil: fact or fiction?', *J. Child Psychology and Psychiatry*, **17** (1976).

41. E. Z. Friedenberg, op cit., p. 24.

42. T. Lidz et al., 'Schism and skew in the families of schizophrenics', *A. J. Psychiatry*, **114** (1957).

43. S. Fleck et al., 'Comparison of parent-child relationships of male and female schizophrenic patients', *Archives of General Psychiatry*, **8** (1963).

44. R. Kellner, *Family Ill Health: an Investigation in General Practice*, Tavistock, 1963, p. 69.

45. N. Kreitman et al., 'Neurosis and marital interaction: IV, personality and symptoms', *B. J. Psychiatry*, **117** (1970).

46. A. Ryle, *Neurosis in the Ordinary Family*, Tavistock, 1967; B. Ineichen, 'Neurotic wives in a modern residential suburb: a sociological profile', *Social Science and Medicine*, **9** (1975).

47. J. Collins et al., 'Neurosis and marital interaction III: family roles and functions', *B. J. Psychiatry*, **119** (1971); I. M. K. Ovenstone, 'Development of neurosis in the wives of neurotic men: II. marital role functions and marital tension', *B. J. Psychiatry*, **122** (1973).
48. C. Rycroft, *Anxiety and Neurosis*, Penguin, 1970, p. 92.
49. One interesting attempt to fill the gap, including Mozart and Picasso among its case studies, is J. Ehrenwald, *Neurosis in the Family and Patterns of Psychosocial Defence*, Harper and Row, 1963.
50. G. W. Brown et al., op. cit.
51. J. H. Scanzoni, *Opportunity and the Family*, Free Press, 1970.
52. J. Grad and P. Sainsbury, 'Mental illness and the family', *Lancet*, **1** (1963) 544–7.
53. S. Hewitt, *The Family and the Handicapped Child*, Allen and Unwin, 1970.
54. D. Hawks, 'Community care: an analysis of assumptions', *B. J. Psychiatry*, **127** (1975).

Chapter 4   Mental illness: a form of social deviance?

1. M. Lader, *Psychiatry on Trial*, Penguin, 1977.
2. For a detailed account of the abuse of psychiatry in Soviet Russia, see S. Block and P. Reddaway, *Russia's Political Hospitals*, Gollancz, 1977; Futura, 1978.
3. T. S. Szasz, 'The psychiatrist as double agent', in A. L. Strauss (ed.), *Where Medicine Fails*, Aldine, 1970.
4. M. Siegler and H. Osmond, *Models of Madness, Models of Medicine*, Harper and Row, 1976.
5. T. Parsons, *The Social System*, Free Press, 1951.
6. R. Sidel, 'Mental diseases in China and their treatment', in T. J. Scheff (ed.), *Labeling Madness*, Prentice Hall, 1975; S. S. Kety, 'Psychiatric concepts and treatment in China', *China Quarterly*, **66** (June 1976).
7. J. W. Eaton and R. J. Weil, *Culture and Mental Disorders*, Free Press, 1955.
8. T. J. Scheff, *Becoming Mentally Ill*, Weidenfeld and Nicolson, 1966.
9. W. L. Tonge et al., 'The prevalence of neurosis in women', *B. J. Soc. Med.*, **4** (1961).
10. M. Shepherd et al., *Psychiatric Illness in General Practice*, Oxford University Press, 1966.
11. C. A. Nathanson, 'Illness and the feminine role: a review', *Social Science and Medicine*, **9** 2 (1975).
12. P. Chesler, *Women and Madness*, Allen Lane, 1974.
13. I. K. Broverman et al., 'Sex-role stereotypes and clinical judgments of mental health', *J. Consulting and Clinical Psychology*, **34**, 1 (1976).
14. P. Chesler, op. cit. p. 65.
15. J. Mitchell, *Psychoanalysis and Feminism*, Allen Lane, 1974.
16. K. Clancy and W. Gove, 'Sex differences in mental illness', *American Journal of Sociology*, **80** 1 (1974).
17. B. P. and B. S. Dohrenwend, 'Sex differences in psychiatric disorder', *American Journal of Sociology*, **81** 6 (1976).
18. C. Smart, *Women, Crime and Criminology*, Routledge and Kegan Paul, 1977, Ch. 6.
19. B. P. and B. S. Dohrenwend, op. cit.

20. A. B. Hollingshead and F. C. Redlich, *Social Class and Mental Illness*, Wiley, 1958.
21. J. H. Scanzoni, *Opportunity and the Family*, Free Press, 1970.
22. G. W. Brown et al., 'Social class and psychiatric disturbance among women in an urban population', *Sociology*, **9** 2 (1975).
23. M. Rutter and N. Madge, *Cycles of Disadvantage*, Heinemann, 1976.
24. D. Rosenblatt and E. A. Suchman, 'The under-utilisation of medical-care services by blue-collarites', in A. Shostak and W. Gomberg (eds), *Blue-Collar World*, Prentice-Hall, 1964.
25. E. Hoffer, *The Ordeal of Change*, Sidgwick and Jackson, 1964, Ch. 1.
26. G. M. Carstairs and J. K. Wing, 'Attitudes of the general public to mental illness', *B. M. J.*, **2** (1958).
27. U. Maclean, 'Community attitudes to mental illness in Edinburgh', *B. J. Prev. Soc. Med.*, **23** (1969).
28. J. Middleton, 'Prejudices and opinions of mental hospital employees regarding mental illness', *A. J. Psychiatry*, **110** (1953).
29. J. Cohen and E. L. Struening, 'Opinions about mental illness in the personnel of two large mental hospitals', *J. Abnormal and Social Psychology*, **64** 5 (1962).
30. S. H. King, *Perception of Illness and Medical Practice*, Russell Sage, 1962, Ch. 5.
31. G. M. Crocetti et al., *Contemporary Attitudes Towards Mental Illness*, Pittsburgh University Press, 1974, Table 4, p. 51.
32. Ibid., Table 20, p. 86.
33. For a thorough review of American research of this topic, see J. Rabkin, 'Public attitudes towards mental illness: a review of the literature', *Schizophrenia Bulletin*, **10** (1974).
34. J. and E. Cumming, 'Mental health education in a Canadian community', in B. D. Paul (ed.), *Health, Culture and Community*, Russell Sage, 1955; J. and E. Cumming, *Closed Ranks*, Harvard University Press, 1957.
35. J. Brockman and C. D'Arcy, 'Correlates of attitudinal social distance towards the mentally ill: a review and re-survey', *Social Psychiatry*, **13** (1978).
36. L. Rootman and H. Lafawe, 'Are popular attitudes to the mentally ill changing?', *A. J. Psychiatry*, **126** (1969).
37. J. Cohen and E. L. Struening, op. cit.
38. J. L. Woodward, 'Changing ideas of mental illness and its treatment', *American Sociological Review*, **16** (1951).
39. Crocetti et al., op. cit., p. 139.
40. S. H. King, op. cit.
41. R. M. Moroney, *The Family and the State*, Longman, 1976.

Postscript.

The following were published too late to be considered here. All add considerably to our knowledge of mental illness.

G. W. Brown and T. O. Harris, *The Social Origins of Depression*, Tavistock, 1978.
M. K. Hinchcliffe et al., *The Melancholy Marriage*, Wiley 1978.
J. K. Wing, *Reasoning About Madness*, Oxford University Press, 1978.

INDEX

Ackerknecht, E. H., 98n
admission rates, 12–13, 29, 32, 34, 39
adolescent crisis, 5–6, 50, 59–61,
    69–70
affection in marriage, 71
agnostic societies, 53
Akan people, 28
alcoholism, 41, 84
Alexander, F. G., 98n
American Psychiatric Association, 81
Andry, R. G., 102n
anxiety, 16, 17, 29, 80
Arie, T., 96n
asylums, 4, 23, 92
atheistic societies, 53
autism, 62–3

Bagley, C., 99n
Bannister, D., 96n
Barnes, M., 96n
Barnett, M., 99n
Baruch, G., 10
Bateson, G., 57–8
Bean, L. L., 100n
Behaviour problems, 37, 90
Berger, P., 103n
Berke, J., 96n
Britchnell, J., 103n
birth control, 87–8
Bleuler, 3, 4
Bloch, S., 104n
Bott, E., 67
Bowlby, J., 54–6, 82
Boyers, R., 102n
Braginsky, B. M., 4
Brill, N. Q., 101n
Brockman, J., 105n

Bromberg, W., 98n
Broverman, I. K., 104n
Brown, G. W., 65, 66, 72, 85, 101n,
    105n
Buck, V. E., 101n
Burgess, E. W. 31

Carstairs, G. M., 105n
Cartwright, A., 100n
Castle, I. M., 99n
Catholics, 51–2
Chave, S., 35
Chesler, P., 80–2, 84
Chester, R., 67
Cheyne, 22–3
Child Guidance Clinics, 49
Childbirth, 63
China, 78–9
Clancy, K., 83
Clare, A. W., 9–10, 47–8
Clausen, J. A., 102n
Clegg, A., 101n
Clout, I., 36, 65
Cohen, J., 91, 105n
Coleman, S. D., 36, 100n
Collier, A., 60
Collins, J., 104n
Comaroff, J., 103n
commuting, 31
Cooper, J. E., 98n
Cornell Medical Index, 19
crime, 32–3, 45–6, 75, 84
Crocetti, G. M., 90–2
Crowcroft, A., 96n
Cullen, 22
Cumming, J. and E., 91
cycle of disadvantage, 85

D'Arcy, C., 105n
Davis, A., 103n
Davis, D. R., 96n, 102n
defensible space, 38, 41
Dennis, N., 101n
depression, 7, 17, 29, 41, 42, 64, 80
Devons, E., 101n
diagnosis, 9, 12, 17–22, 77
  gender differences in, 84
  general practitioners, 14–15
  social class differences in, 84–6
  see also schizophrenia
Diploma in Psychological Medicine, 22
distribution of mental illness, 30–33
divorce, 67, 94
Dohrenwend, B. P. and B. S., 16, 20–1, 31, 83–4
dominance in marriage, 57, 71
double-bind, 56–60
Dreitzel, H. P., 103n
Drewery, J., 25
Duff, E., 101n
Duhl, L. J., 100n
Dunham, H. W., 31
Durkheim, E., 29, 51–3

Eagleton, T., 47
Earls, F., 102n
Eastwood, F., 96n
Eaton, J. W., 50, 79, 97n
education, 48–50
Ehrewald, J., 104n
Ennis, B. J., 97n
epidemiology, 2, 13–17, 77, 83, 84
Erikson, E. H., 69
estates, local authority housing, 33
Esterson, A., 59–61, 69, 82
ethnic group, 41–3
extended families, 95

Fanning, D. M., 100n
Faris, R. E. L., 31
Farringdon, D. P., 102n
Ferguson, T., 99n
flats, high-rise, 36
Fleck, S., 103n
Frankenberg, R., 99n
Fraser, M., 29
Freeman, H. D., 47
Freeman, W., 101n
Freud, S., 4, 61, 81–2

Fried, M., 100n, 101n
Friedenberg, E. Z., 69, 102n
Fromm-Reichmann, F., 57
Fry, E., 55

Gath, D., 101n
General Health Questionnaire, 20
general practitioners, 13–15
George III, King, 23
Gillis, A. R., 100n
Gittus, E., 99n, 100n
Glasser, W., 10
Gluckman, M., 101n
Goffman, E., 10
Goldberg, D., 20
Goldie, N., 98n
Gomberg, W., 105n
Gove, W., 83
Grad, J., 104n
Grimes, J. A., 97n
Grimker, R. R., 97n
Grunebaum, H., 63, 103n
Gurin, G., 97n

Hall, P., 100n
Hardman, R. A., 100n
Hare, E. H., 32, 34–5, 102n
Harris, T. O., 105n
Hart, N., 103n
Hawks, D., 104n
healers, non-medical, 27–8, 42, 51
Helzer, J. E., 19
Hemsi, L. K., 101n
Henry, W. E., 24
Hewitt, S., 104n
Hicks, D., 15
Hinchliffe, M. K., 105n
Hinkle, L. E., 101n
Hirsch, S. R., 57, 59, 61–2
Hoffer, E., 88–9
Hole, V., 100n
Hollinghead, A. B., 25, 26, 84, 100n
Hooper, D., 100n
Horobin, G., 103n
hospitalisation, 10, 18, 47, 50, 76, 92, 94
housing, 31–9, 86–7
Hunter, R., 98n
Hutterites, 16, 50, 79
hysteria, 72

Ineichen, B., 100n, 103n
isolation of nuclear family, 65–9, 73

Jackson, B., 101n
Jefferys, M., 100n
Jehovah's Witnesses, 50–1
Jephcott, P., 100n
Jews, 52–3
Jolley, D. J., 96n
Jones, K., 98n

Kanner, 62
Kellner, H., 103n
Kellner, R., 70
Kendell, R. E., 5, 7
Kesey, K., 85
Kessel, N., 98n
Kety, S. S., 99n, 104n
Kiev, A., 17, 101n
King, S. H., 90, 92, 105n
Kirby, J., 99n
Kluckhohn, C., 97n
Kohn, M., 102n
Kornhauser, A., 44
Kraepelin, 3, 4
Kreitman, N., 25, 103n

labelling, 11, 77–8
Lader, M., 76
Lafawe, H., 105n
Laing, R. D., 4, 9, 57, 59–61, 69, 78, 82
Langner, T. S., 97n
lay attitudes to mental illness, 89–92
Leff, J. P., 57, 59, 61–2
Leighton, A. H., 97n, 101n
Leighton, D. C., 97n
Lidz, T., 70
Litwach, T. R., 97n
Lomas, P., 59
Lyons, H. A., 29

Macalpine, T., 98n
Maclean, U., 105n
Madge, N., 85
manic depressive psychosis, 7, 31, 83
marriage, 65–8, 70, 71–3, 94
Marsden, D., 101n
Martin, F. M., 99n, 100n
Maskin, M., 102n
Masserman, J. H., 102n
maternal deprivation, 54–6
Maule, H. G., 99n
Mays, J. B., 99n
McGowen, P., 101n

M'Gonigle, G. C. M., 99n
measurement of mental illness, 12–17, 30–2, 35
Megson, B., 101n
mental handicap, 2
Michael, S. T., 97n
Middleton, J., 105n
migraine, 8
migration, 47
MIND, 93
Mitchell, A. R. K., 5
Mitchell, J., 81–2
models of mental illness, 11–12, 77–9, 94
Mogey, J., 100n
Moore, N. C., 100n
Morel, 3
Morgan, H. G., 99n
Moroney, R. M., 105n
Morris, R. N., 100n
Morris, T., 33
moving house, 38–9
Mowbray, R. M., 14
murder, 63–4, 76
Musgrove, F., 101n
Myers, J. K., 100n

Nathanson, C. A., 104n
National Council for Civil Liberties, 28
National Council for the Single Woman and her Dependants, 68
neuroses, 7, 22–3, 36, 65
  in families, 70–2
  by gender, 79, 83–4
New Towns, 35–6
Newman, O., 38, 41
North, M., 98n

Odegaard, O., 101n
one-parent families, 95
Ophelia, 3
Orrill, R., 102n
Osmond, H., 11, 77–8, 102n
Ovenstone, I. M. K., 104n

Paffenbarger, R. S., 103n
Pallis, D. J., 98n
parents, 95
Park, R. E., 31
Parkes, C. M., 103n
Parkinson's disease, 5

Parsons, T., 104n
paternal deprivation, 56
Patients' Association, 28
Paul, B. D., 105n
Paykel, E. S., 103n
personality disorder, 7, 84
Pettigrew, M. G., 99n
Phillips, L., 97n
Pinel, 22
Pizzey, E., 64
political structure, 28, 76–7
Poor Law, 23
Positive Mental Health, 26–7
Power, M., 101n
powerlessness, 38, 41, 86
Preventive Psychiatry, 26
Primrose, E. J. R., 100n
Protestants, 51–2
pseudopatients, 18
Psychiatric Rehabilitation
    Association, 32, 41
psychiatrists, 13
    careers of, 24
    changing role of, 89
    and double standard, 81
    as gaolers, 24, 76–7
    ideologies of, 24–7, 93–4
    suicide rate of, 45
    in universities, 27
psychopaths, 7
psychoses, 2–7, 31, 35, 64, 84
psychosomatic illnesses, 8
Pugh, T. F., 103n

Rabkin, J., 105n
Reddaway, P., 104n
Redlich, F. C., 25, 26, 84, 100n
Reed, D., 96n
religion, 16, 50–3
residential area, 30–9
Resnich, P. J., 103n
Richman, N., 100n
Riessman, F., 101n
Roberts, B. H., 100n
Robinson, H., 100n
Rogow, A. A., 24
Rootman, L., 105n
Rosenblatt, D., 105n
Rosenhan, D. L., 97n
Roth, M., 5
Royal College of Psychiatrists, 22
rural-urban differences, 30–1

Rutter, M., 55–6, 62, 63, 85, 103n
Rwegellera, G. G. C., 101n
Rycroft, C., 72
Ryle, A., 101n, 103n

Sainsbury, P., 33, 98n, 99n, 104n
Scanzoni, J., 85, 104n
Scheff, T. J., 11, 13, 78
schizophrenia, 2–6, 41, 42, 47–8, 51,
    84
 —diagnosis of, 5, 20, 62, 76
 —and family dynamics, 57–62
Scientologists, 28, 51
Seager, C. P., 103n
Sedgwick, P., 58–9
Selesnick, S. T., 98n
self-assessment, 15
self-esteem, 72, 85
self-harm, non-fatal deliberate, 33
senile dementia, 6
sex differences in mental illness, 14,
    79–84
sexual behaviour, 87–8
Shaw, C., 33
Shaw, G. K., 34–5, 102n
Shepherd, M., 14, 79–80
Shostak, A., 105n
Sidel, R., 104n
Siegler, M., 11, 77–8, 102n
Simmons, O. G., 47
Singer, M. T., 61
Skultans, V., 98n, 102n
Smart, C., 84
Smith, S. M., 103n
Sobey, F., 99n
social change, 87–95
social class, 40–1, 84–7
social distance, 90–1
Spencer, J., 102n
spiralists, 43
Spiritualists, 51
Srole, L., 97n, 102n
Stein, Z., 103n
Stevenson, A., 100n
Stoffelmayer, B. E., 98n
Storr, A., 98n
Strauss, A. L., 25, 26, 104n
Struening, E. L., 91, 105n
students, 50, 76–7
Suchman, E. A., 105n
suicide, 33, 51–2, 80
    see also psychiatrists

Susser, M. W., 101n, 103n
Sutherland, J. D., 103n
Szasz, T. S., 4–5, 9–10, 27, 80

Taylor, Lord, 35
teenagers, 57, 61, 69
Temerlin, M. K., 97n
Toker, E., 101n
Tonge, W. L., 79
Toynbee, P., 44
tranquillisers, 29
Treacher, A., 10
Trevelyan, M. H., 96n
Trotter, 23
Tuke, S., 23
Tunstall, J., 101n

unemployment, 94

violence, 28–9, 63–4, 79
Viscott, D., 24

Wadsworth, M., 97n
Wallis, R., 51, 99n
Walton, H. J., 25

Watson, W., 101n
weddings, 94
Weil, R. J., 50, 79, 97n
Weissman, M. M., 103n
West Indians, 42–3, 48
widowhood, 68
Wilder, J., 101n
Willmott, P., 34, 65
Wilner, D. M., 100n
Wilson, B., 99n
Wing, J. K., 63, 98n, 105n
Wing, L., 102n
Wolff, H. G., 101n
Wolff, S., 63
Woodward, J. L., 91
Wootton, B., 55
work, 43–7, 86, 88
Wynne, L. C., 61

Yancey, W. L., 100n
York Retreat, 23
Yoruba people, 17, 28
Young, M., 34, 65

Zigler, E., 97n

SOCIAL RESEARCH

The Limitations of Social Research
Prof. M. D. Shipman
University of Warwick

Social Research Design
Prof. E. Krausz
University of Newcastle
and
S. H. Miller
City University

Sources of Official Data
Kathleen Pickett
University of Liverpool

History of Social Research Methods
Gary Easthope
University of East Anglia

Deciphering Data
Jonathan Silvey
University of Nottingham

Forthcoming titles will include:

The Philosophy of Social Research
John Hughes
University of Lancaster

Techniques of Data Collection
Stephen Ackroyd
and
John Hughes
University of Lancaster

112

SOCIAL PROCESSES

Bureaucracy
Dennis Warwick
University of Leeds

Social Control
C. Ken Watkins
University of Leeds

Communication
Prof. Denis McQuail
University of Amsterdam

Stratification
Prof. R. K. Kelsall
University of Sheffield
and
H. Kelsall

Industrialism
Barry Turner
University of Exeter

Social Change
Anthony Smith
University of Reading

Socialisation
Graham White
University of Liverpool

Forthcoming titles will include:

Social Conflict
Prof. John Rex
University of Warwick

211
213
274
201

959
272

12 3 1
2 8 0

15 1 1
2 7 1
2 4 0
1 8 9

2 2 1 1
7 2